Application of B & K Equipment

to

FREQUENCY ANALYSIS

by

R. B. Randall, B. Tech., B. A.

September 1977

2nd edition   1st print

ISBN 87 87355 14 0

II

CONTENTS

FREQUENCY ANALYSIS

1. INTRODUCTION

The object of frequency analysis is to break down a complex signal into its components at various frequencies, and it can be shown that this is possible for all practical signals (Ref. 1.1). The word "components" can be interpreted in several different ways, however, and it is important to clarify the differences between them.

Mathematicians and theoretical engineers tend to interpret "components" as the results of a Fourier Analysis, while practical engineers often think in terms of measurements made with filters tuned to different frequencies. It is one of the purposes of this book to clarify the relationships between these two approaches. Another is to give a simple pictorial interpretation of Fourier analysis which greatly facilitates the understanding of fundamental relationships, in particular the connection between mathematical theory and practical analysis by both analog and digital means.

The approach taken is to consider frequency components as vectors rotating in a complex plane rather than as sums of sines and cosines. A typical (co-)sinusoidal component is represented as the sum of two contra-rotating vectors rather than as the projection on the real axis of a single rotating vector. The advantage of this is not only that it simplifies the pictorial representation developed here, but also that it is mathematically more general and more consistent. In particular, it eliminates the problem of deciding when to take the real part of a complex mathematical expression, as arises in the approach based on projection.

In both approaches a considerable simplification of the mathematics arises from the fact that a vector (having two components e. g. amplitude and phase) can be represented as a single complex variable and because differentiation and integration of such complex variables are so simple. It is assumed that the reader is familiar with the basic relationships between complex exponentials and sinusoids, but a brief résumé of the most important relationships is given at the start of Chapter 2.

Chapter 2 continues with a discussion of Fourier analysis, first the various forms taken by the Fourier transform, then the important practical consideration of bandwidth. This leads into a discussion of the different types of signal encountered in practice, and how they appear in spectral and other representations. Finally, the very important subject of convolution is treated in some detail. It is shown how the output of a linear physical system is obtained by convolving the input signal with the impulse response of the system and how this rather complicated operation transforms by the Fourier transform to a multiplication (which in turn becomes an addition in the normal logarithmic representation of spectra). Other applications of this so-called "Convolution Theorem" are also given.

Chapter 3 is entitled "Analog Analysis" but in fact is somewhat more general. After a discussion of the function and properties of the basic elements of an analog analysis system, a procedure is indicated which allows the optimal selection of analysis parameters in a logical way. At first the discussion is limited to stationary signals, but then extended to non-stationary signals, both continuous and transient.

Chapter 4 is a brief discussion of digital filtering and in particular the advantages of recursive digital filters for real-time constant percentage bandwidth analysis. Because of the similarity of digital filters to their analog counterparts, considerable reference is made to the results of Chapter 3.

Chapter 5 introduces another digital analysis method, the so-called Fast Fourier Transform (FFT), which since its introduction in 1965 has revolutionized signal analysis. In Chapter 5 the discussion is limited to simple spectrum analysis of a single channel signal, for direct comparison with the methods of previous chapters. It is seen that FFT (as for the Time Compression method of Chapter 3) is best adapted to constant bandwidth analysis on a linear frequency scale.

Chapter 6 is a brief introduction to a number of other analysis techniques which have been made possible, or in any case very much simpler, by the use of FFT techniques. These include zoom FFT, correlation, coherence and cepstrum techniques. The selection is by no means exhaustive, but gives an idea of the almost explosive development which has occurred in recent years.

Because of the newness of some of the topics of Chapter 6, examples of applications have been given, while in the rest of the book not much has been said about applications; it being assumed that a reader already had a need for frequency analysis, and only required information on how to obtain the results. Even so, it is perhaps desirable to give a brief survey of the major reasons for the widespread use of frequency analysis.

Without a doubt the major reason is that many physical and biological systems only respond to a limited range of frequencies. For example, the human ear only perceives sound within the range 20 Hz — 20 kHz, while for estimating the effects of "whole body vibration" the range is rather more restricted (typically 1 — 80 Hz). Quite often physical systems, be they electrical circuits or civil engineering structures, only have strong resonances within a limited frequency range, and hence the study of their behaviour when subjected to an external excitation can be restricted to this frequency range, thus greatly simplifying the problem. As mentioned previously, the calculation of the response of a linear system reduces in the frequency domain to a simple multiplication. An input at a given frequency gives an output only at that same frequency, and thus frequency analysis permits treating each frequency individually without regard to what is happening at other frequencies.

Sometimes frequency analysis is used to make a picture clearer. Quite often the "noisiness" of a signal is contained mainly in its phase spectrum, the power spectrum being relatively stable, and quite often it is the power spectrum which gives most information with respect to "average" effects.

The frequency content of a signal can often be used diagnostically; for example in tracing the source of a noise problem to a particular machine, or of a mechanical problem to a particular rotating component.

On the other hand it must be kept in mind that frequency analysis is not a universal panacea. In enhancing periodic events it tends to smear out individual ones; for example, one obtains information about tooth-meshing frequencies in a gearbox but tends to lose information about individual gear teeth.

Even so, there are many problems where frequency analysis reigns supreme, and it is hoped that the information in this book will help to avoid some of the pitfalls which can be encountered, so that the data obtained by frequency analysis are correct (or at least have a known degree of accuracy) before they are applied to the solution of a practical problem.

2. THEORETICAL FREQUENCY ANALYSIS

2.1. BASIC CONCEPTS

2.1.1. Complex Notation

As mentioned in the Introduction, the approach to Fourier analysis used here is based on the representation of frequency components as rotating vectors, these in turn being represented mathematically as complex exponentials. A short résumé is given here of some of the most important relationships which will be used later in the text.

Figure 2.1 represents a two-dimensional vector F in the so-called "complex plane". This has a "real" component a directed along the "Real Axis" and an "imaginary" component jb directed along the "Imaginary Axis". The vector as a whole is represented as the sum of these, viz.:

$$F = a + jb \tag{2.1}$$

Note that b alone, as a real number, would lie along the Real Axis, but that multiplication by j has the effect of rotating it through $\pi/2$ radians. Accordingly, a further multiplication by j would result in a further rotation through $\pi/2$ so that the vector of length b would then lie along the negative Real Axis as shown in Figure 2.1. Hence, multiplication by j^2 corresponds to a multiplication by -1 and j can thus be interpreted as $\sqrt{-1}$.

Note that the complex plane shown here is turned through 90° as compared with the conventional representation with the Real Axis horizontal. This is done purely to simplify interpretation of the Real Axis as being in the plane of the paper rather than at right angles to it in 3-dimensional diagrams (e. g. Fig. 2.4).

5

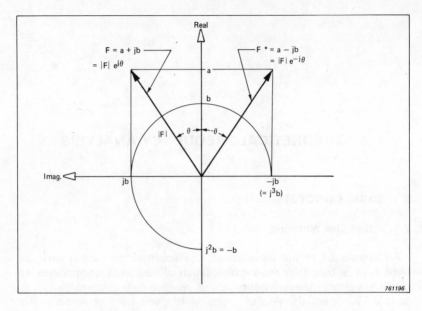

Fig.2.1. Complex notation for a 2-dimensional vector

In many cases it is desirable to represent F in terms of its amplitude $|F|$ and phase angle θ instead of its real and imaginary components, and from Fig.2.1 it can be seen that the relationships between these two sets of coordinates are:

$$a = |F| \cos \theta$$
$$b = |F| \sin \theta$$
$$|F| = \sqrt{a^2 + b^2} \qquad (2.2)$$
$$\theta = \tan^{-1}\left(\frac{b}{a}\right)$$

From equations (2.1) and (2.2) it follows that:

$$F = |F| (\cos \theta + j \sin \theta) \qquad (2.3)$$

and since it is well-known (Euler's relation) that:

$$\cos \theta + j \sin \theta = e^{j\theta} \qquad (2.4)$$

6

the most concise way of representing F in terms of its amplitude and phase is as the complex exponential

$$F = |F|\, e^{j\theta} \tag{2.5}$$

As a point of terminology, Fig.2.1 also illustrates what is meant by F^*, the "complex conjugate" of F. This is seen to be the mirror image of F around the real axis. Thus, the real part and amplitude have the same sign while the imaginary part and phase angle have opposite sign. The absolute values of the equivalent components are the same.

In general in this book we will be considering uniformly rotating vectors, i. e. vectors whose amplitude $|F|$ is a constant and whose phase angle θ is a linearly varying function of time

$$i.e. \quad \theta = \omega t + \phi$$

where ω is a constant angular frequency (in radians/s) and ϕ is the "initial" phase angle at time zero.

Normally, the frequency will be expressed as circular frequency f in revolutions/s (Hertz) rather than ω in radians/s and thus

$$\theta = 2\pi f t + \phi \tag{2.6}$$

It follows from the above that $e^{j\phi}$ is a unit vector (amplitude = 1) with angular orientation ϕ, and $e^{j\theta}$ (where θ is as defined in (2.6.)) is a unit vector rotating at frequency f Hz and with angular orientation ϕ at time zero.

Vector multiplication is simplest when the vectors are expressed in the form of equation (2.5) and for two vectors $F_1 (= |F_1| e^{j\theta_1})$ and $F_2 (= |F_2| e^{j\theta_2})$ is obtained simply as:

$$\begin{aligned} F_1 \cdot F_2 &= |F_1| e^{j\theta_1} \cdot |F_2| e^{j\theta_2} \\ &= |F_1| \cdot |F_2| e^{j(\theta_1 + \theta_2)} \end{aligned} \tag{2.7}$$

i. e. the amplitude of the product is equal to the product of the two amplitudes while the phase is equal to the sum of the phases.

In particular, multiplication by a fixed unit vector $e^{j\phi}$ has no effect on the amplitude but adds ϕ to the phase angle (i. e. rotates the vector through an angle ϕ) while multiplication by the rotating unit vector $e^{j2\pi ft}$ causes a vector to rotate at frequency f.

2.1.2. Delta Functions●

Another mathematical concept of which considerable use will be made is the Dirac delta function, also known as the "unit impulse". A typical delta function, located on an X-axis at $x = x_0$ may be represented as $\delta(x—x_0)$. It has the property that its value is zero everywhere except at $x = x_0$, where its value is infinite. It has the further property, however, that the result of integrating over any range of the X-axis which includes x_0 is a unit area. It can be considered as the limiting case of any pulse with unit area whose length is made infinitely short at the same time as its height is made infinitely large, while retaining the unit area. The unit delta function can be weighted by a scaling factor (with or without physical dimensions) so that the result of integrating over it gives the value of the weighting. The delta function provides a means of treating functions which are infinitely narrowly localised on an axis at the same time as other functions which are distributed along the axis. A typical case is that of a single discrete frequency component which is to be represented in terms of its "power spectral density" (see Section 2.2.5.). Because of the infinitely narrow localisation of a discrete frequency component on a frequency axis, its spectral **density** (power per unit frequency) will be infinitely high, but since it represents a certain finite power, it can be considered as a delta function weighted by this value of power.

2.2. FOURIER ANALYSIS

The mathematical basis of frequency analysis is the Fourier Transform which takes different forms depending on the type of signal analyzed. All have in common that the signal is assumed to be composed of a number (perhaps an infinite number) of (co-)sinusoidal components at various frequencies, each having a given amplitude and initial phase. A typical (co-)sinusoidal component with amplitude A, initial phase ϕ and circular frequency f^{Δ} is illustrated in Fig.2.2(a).

● Ref. 1.1 contains a mathematically rigorous discussion of delta functions and their relationship to Fourier Analysis

$^{\Delta}$ $f = \dfrac{1}{T}$ where T is the periodic time

The representation of Fig.2.2(a) has the disadvantage that both time and phase angle are represented along the X-axis and can thus be easily confused. Furthermore, the mathematically useful concept of negative frequency is either meaningless or in any case unclear.

Fig.2.2(b) illustrates another representation of the same sinusoidal component, this time as the vector sum of two contra-rotating vectors, each with amplitude $A/2$. One has initial phase angle ϕ and rotates with frequency f while the other has initial phase $-\phi$ and rotates with frequency $-f$. The concept of negative frequency now has the clear physical interpretation of indicating a negative rate of change of phase angle, and is necessary in order to indicate rotation in opposite directions.

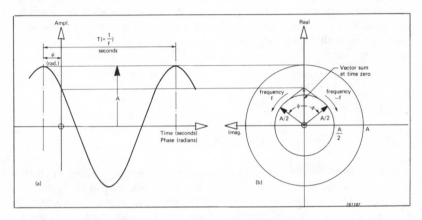

Fig.2.2. (a) Typical sinusoidal component A cos (2 πft + φ)
(b) Representation as sum of contra-rotating vectors

Fig.2.2(b) represents the position of the vectors at time zero, but it can be seen that as they rotate with time, the vector sum will always be real (the imaginary parts cancel out) and will trace out the sinusoidal curve illustrated in Fig.2.2(a).

The equivalence of the two forms is contained in the mathematical identity:

$$A \cos \theta = \frac{A}{2} (e^{j\theta} + e^{-j\theta}) \qquad (2.8)$$

where $\theta = (2\pi ft + \phi)$ as in Equation (2.6)

9

2.2.1. Fourier Series

The application of this to Fourier analysis can be understood by considering the case of Fourier series expansion of a periodic function.

If $g(t)$ is a periodic function, i. e.

$$g(t) = g(t + nT) \qquad (2.9)$$

where T is the periodic time
and n is any integer

then it can be shown (Ref. 2.1) that it can be represented as a sum of sinusoidal components (or equivalently rotating vectors) at equally spaced frequencies kf_1 where f_1 $(=1/T)$ is the reciprocal of the periodic time and k is an integer (including zero and negative integers). The k th component is obtained from the integral

$$G(f_k) = \frac{1}{T} \int_{-T/2}^{T/2} g(t) e^{-j2\pi f_k t} \, dt \qquad (2.10)$$

where $f_k = kf_1$

(i. e. the k th harmonic of f_1)

It is worthwhile examining in detail what this integral achieves. If the signal $g(t)$ contains a component rotating at a frequency of f_k, then multiplication by the unit vector $e^{-j2\pi f_k t}$ (which rotates at $-f_k$) annuls the rotation of the signal component such that it integrates with time to a finite value. (Fig. 2.3(a)).

All components at other frequencies will still rotate even after multiplication by $e^{-j2\pi f_k t}$ and will thus integrate to zero over the periodic time. (Fig. 2.3(b)).

It is of interest here that the effect of multiplying the signal by $e^{-j2\pi f_k t}$ is in fact to shift the frequency origin to frequency f_k and thus all the original harmonics will still be harmonics of the modified time signal.

Thus equation (2.10) has the effect of extracting from $g(t)$ the components it contains which rotate at each frequency f_k. At the same time, as illustrated in Fig. 2.3(a) it "freezes" the phase angle of each as that

10

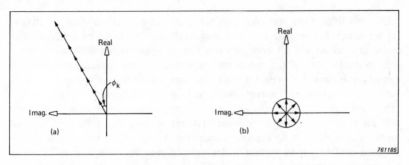

Fig.2.3. (a) Integration of a non-rotating vector to a finite value
(b) Integration of a rotating vector to zero

existing at time zero (when $e^{-j2\pi f_k t} = 1$). The actual position of each vector at any other time t can thus be obtained by multiplying its initial value $G(f_k)$ by the oppositely rotating unit vector $e^{j2\pi f_k t}$ and the total signal $g(t)$ will thus be the (vector) sum of all these vectors in their instantaneous positions, i. e.

$$g(t) = \sum_{k=-\infty}^{\infty} G(f_k)e^{j2\pi f_k t} \qquad (2.11)$$

The series of (complex) values $G(f_k)$ are known as the spectrum components of $g(t)$ and since there is an amplitude and phase (or equivalently real and imaginary part) associated with each one, a full representation requires three dimensions. Fig.2.4 illustrates such a 3-dimensional representation of a typical spectrum.

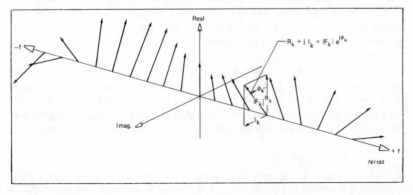

Fig.2.4. 3-dimensional representation of the spectrum of a periodic function

11

Several important remarks can be made at this stage. One is that a signal which is periodic in the time domain has a spectrum which is discrete and in which all components fall at frequencies which are integral multiples of the fundamental frequency f_1. The reason for this can easily be understood. The time for one rotation of the vector at the fundamental frequency f_1 corresponds to one period time T. Since all the other vectors rotate at speeds which are integer multiples of f_1 they will all rotate an integer number of turns during this time and will all have returned to their starting positions. Thus, after time T the whole process will begin to repeat itself exactly and the function will clearly be periodic with period T.

Another important observation is that if the function $g(t)$ is real-valued (as it generally will be in the case of physical signals) then each component at frequency f_k must be matched by a component at $-f_k$ which has equal amplitude but opposite phase (or equivalently equal real part and opposite imaginary part). In this way the imaginary parts at all frequencies will always cancel and the resultant will always be real. This is obvious for the single sinusoidal component of Fig.2.2 and applies to each component in the more general case. Mathematically, it can be said that the spectrum of a real-valued function is "conjugate even" i. e.

$$G(f_k) = G^*(-f_k) \qquad (2.12)$$

where G^* is the complex conjugate of G.

One immediate result of this is that since the series of imaginary parts (or equivalently phase angles) is antisymmetric around zero frequency, then the zero frequency (or DC) component has zero phase angle and is always real, which is intuitively obvious. Fig.2.4 has been drawn to represent such a conjugate even spectrum.

A very important relationship concerns the distribution with frequency of the power content of the signal. The instantaneous power● of the time signal $g(t)$ is equal to $[g(t)]^2$ and the mean power over one period (and thus over any number of periods) is given by integrating the instantaneous value over one period and dividing by the periodic time.

● The word "power" is here used in the sense of a squared variable (independent of the units of that variable) and is thus only related to physical power by a dimensioned scaling constant

Thus,

$$P_{mean} = \frac{1}{T} \int_0^T \{g(t)\}^2 \, dt \qquad (2.13)$$

For the typical sinusoidal component $A_k \cos (2\pi f_k t + \phi_k)$ this results in

$$P_{mean} = \frac{1}{T} \int_0^T A_k{}^2 \cos^2(2\pi f_k t + \phi_k) \, dt$$

$$= \frac{A_k{}^2}{T} \int_0^T \frac{1}{2} - \frac{1}{2} \cos 2(2\pi f_k t + \phi_k) \, dt$$

$$= \frac{A_k{}^2}{2}$$

since the sinusoidal part integrates to zero over 2 periods.

This is the well-known result for the mean square value of a sinusoid of peak amplitude A_k and results in a root mean square (RMS) value of $A_k / \sqrt{2}$ (i. e. $0,707 A_k$).

It will be found that the power content at each frequency is given directly by the square of the amplitude of the Fourier series component. We have seen (Fig.2.2) that except for the DC component the amplitude of $G(f_k)$ is $A_k/2$, where A_k is the peak amplitude of the k th sinusoid, and thus the square of this is $A_k^2/4$. Since the amplitude spectrum is even, the negative frequency component (from $G(-f_k)$) will also be $A_k^2/4$, and thus the total power associated with frequency f_k will be $A_k{}^2/2$, the same as obtained in the time domain. The total power can thus be obtained either by integrating the squared instantaneous signal amplitude with time (and dividing by this time) or by summing the squared amplitudes of all the frequency components. This is one manifestation of the so-called "Parseval's Theorem" (Ref. 2.1).

The spectrum of squared amplitudes (all real) is known as the "power spectrum", and this is often the most useful part of the whole spectrum. However, since the initial phase information is lost, it is not possible to resynthesize the original time signal from the power spectrum.

Fig.2.5(a) illustrates the 2-sided power spectrum corresponding to Fig.2.4, and Fig.2.5(b) the 1-sided power spectrum obtained by adding the negative frequency components to their positive counterparts (thus doubling them). This is the normal representation of the power spectrum and that corresponding to measurements with practical filters,

13

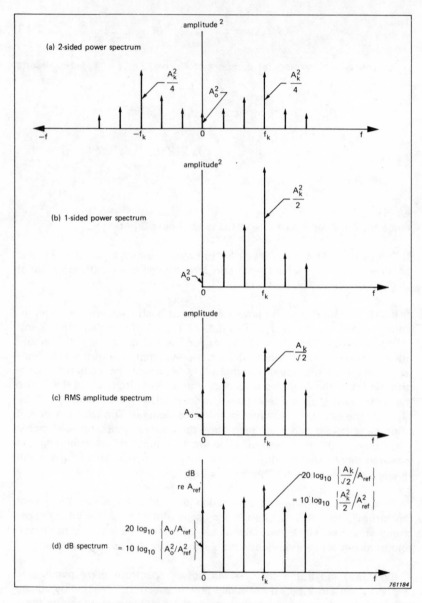

Fig. 2.5. Various spectrum representations

since the latter pass positive and negative frequency contributions equally. Fig.2.5(c) shows the spectrum of RMS values (the square root of the values in 2.5(b)) while Fig.2.5(d) shows the dB amplitude spectrum, which is defined alternatively as $10 \log_{10}$ (Mean square) or $20 \log_{10}$ (RMS) which of course gives the same result in a particular case. The values inside the brackets must be ratios with respect to a specified reference level. Note that the DC component is the same in both the 1-sided and 2-sided representations, since the total power at zero frequency is contained in this one component.

2.2.2. Fourier Transform

All the above results apply to periodic signals but it is possible to extend equation (2.10) to a more general case by letting $T \to \infty$, in which case the spacing $1/T$ between the harmonics tends to zero and $G(f)$ becomes a continuous function of f. It can be shown (Ref. 2.1) that equation (2.10) tends to

$$G(f) = \int_{-\infty}^{\infty} g(t)e^{-j2\pi ft}\, dt \qquad (2.14)$$

and equation (2.11) becomes

$$g(t) = \int_{-\infty}^{\infty} G(f)e^{j2\pi ft}\, df \qquad (2.15)$$

Equation (2.14) is known as the "forward" transform and equation (2.15) as the "inverse" transform while together they form the "Fourier Transform Pair". It can be seen that they are almost symmetrical. The only difference is the sign of the exponent of e. The most important thing about the symmetry is that results which apply to transformation in one direction generally also apply to transformation in the other direction. Fig.2.6 compares the Fourier Integral Transform with Fourier Series and other degenerate forms which are to be discussed.

2.2.3. Sampled Time Functions

Another form of the Fourier Transform pair applies to sampled time functions, i. e. functions which are represented by a "Time-Series", a sequence of values at discrete equi-spaced points in time. This case is becoming very important with the increase in digital processing of data.

15

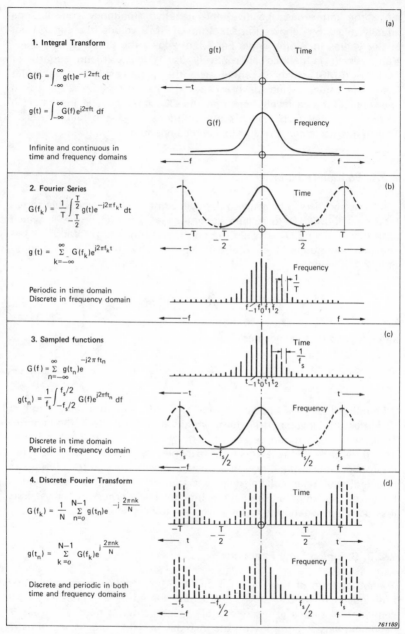

1. Integral Transform

$$G(f) = \int_{-\infty}^{\infty} g(t)e^{-j\,2\pi ft}\,dt$$

$$g(t) = \int_{-\infty}^{\infty} G(f)e^{j2\pi ft}\,df$$

Infinite and continuous in
time and frequency domains

g(t)   Time

G(f)   Frequency

(a)

2. Fourier Series

$$G(f_k) = \frac{1}{T}\int_{-\frac{T}{2}}^{\frac{T}{2}} g(t)e^{-j2\pi f_k t}\,dt$$

$$g(t) = \sum_{k=-\infty}^{\infty} G(f_k)e^{j2\pi f_k t}$$

Periodic in time domain
Discrete in frequency domain

Time

Frequency

$\frac{1}{T}$

$f_{-1}f_0 f_1 f_2$

(b)

3. Sampled functions

$$G(f) = \sum_{n=-\infty}^{\infty} g(t_n)e^{-j2\pi ft_n}$$

$$g(t_n) = \frac{1}{f_s}\int_{-f_s/2}^{f_s/2} G(f)e^{j2\pi ft_n}\,df$$

Discrete in time domain
Periodic in frequency domain

Time

$\frac{1}{f_s}$

$t_{-1}t_0 t_1 t_2$

Frequency

$-f_s$ $-f_s/2$ $f_s/2$ f_s

(c)

4. Discrete Fourier Transform

$$G(f_k) = \frac{1}{N}\sum_{n=0}^{N-1} g(t_n)e^{-j\frac{2\pi nk}{N}}$$

$$g(t_n) = \sum_{k=0}^{N-1} G(f_k)e^{j\frac{2\pi nk}{N}}$$

Discrete and periodic in both
time and frequency domains

Time

Frequency

$-f_s$ $-f_s/2$ $f_s/2$ f_s

(d)

761189

Fig.2.6. Various forms of the Fourier transform

It can be seen that this is a situation which is the reverse of the Fourier Series case (as illustrated in Fig.2.6(b)) and because of the symmetry of the Fourier transform pair, it happens that the spectrum becomes periodic, with a period equal to the sampling frequency f_s (the reciprocal of the time interval Δt between samples). This situation is represented in Fig.2.6(c), and the reason for the periodicity will become clear in the following discussion of the Discrete Fourier Transform.

The particular form the Fourier Transform takes for sampled time functions is as follows:

$$G(f) = \sum_{n=-\infty}^{\infty} g(t_n)e^{-j2\pi f t_n} \tag{2.16}$$

$$g(t_n) = \frac{1}{f_s} \int_{-f_s/2}^{f_s/2} G(f)e^{j2\pi f t_n}\, df \tag{2.17}$$

where $t_n = n\,\Delta t$, i.e. the time corresponding to the n th time sample.

2.2.4. Discrete Fourier Transform

The final possibility occurs when the functions are sampled in both time and frequency domains as illustrated in Fig.2.6(d). Because of the sampling, it is evident that both time signal and frequency spectrum are implicitly periodic in this case, and this periodicity (or "circularity") leads to some interesting effects which will be discussed later.

The forward transform now takes the form●

$$G(k) = \frac{1}{N} \sum_{n=0}^{N-1} g(n)e^{-j\frac{2\pi kn}{N}} \tag{2.18}$$

and the inverse transform takes the form●

$$g(n) = \sum_{k=0}^{N-1} G(k)e^{j\frac{2\pi kn}{N}} \tag{2.19}$$

● Note that for convenience the time and frequency functions have in this case not been made symmetrical about the origin, but because of the periodicity of each, the second half also represents the negative half period to the left of the origin. Note also that parameter k refers to frequency f_k and n to time t_n

Because the infinite continuous integrals of Equations (2.14) and (2.15) have been replaced by finite sums, the above transform pair, known as the "Discrete Fourier Transform" or DFT, is much better adapted to digital computations. Even so, it can be seen that in order to obtain N frequency components from N time samples (or vice versa) requires N^2 complex multiplications. A calculation procedure, known as the "Fast Fourier Transform" or FFT algorithm, which obtains the same result with a number of complex multiplications of the order of $N log_2 N$, is discussed in detail in Chapter 5. The reduction factor in computation time is thus of the order of $N / log_2 N$, which for the typical case of $N = 1024\,(2^{10})$ is more than 100.

However, while leaving the FFT till later, it is useful at this stage to look at the properties of the DFT, since this gives an insight into many fundamental concepts, e. g. sampling theory. One way of interpreting equation (2.18) is as the following matrix equation:

$$\overline{G}_k = \frac{1}{N} \mathbf{A}\, \overline{g}_n \qquad (2.20)$$

where $\overline{G}_k$ is a column array representing the N complex frequency components,
$1/N$ is a simple scaling factor,
$\mathbf{A}$ is a square matrix of unit vectors and
$\overline{g}_n$ is a column array representing the N time samples.
For the particular case of $N = 8$, the equation (2.20) may be visualized as follows:

$$
\begin{bmatrix} G_0 \\ G_1 \\ G_2 \\ G_3 \\ G_4 \\ G_5 \\ G_6 \\ G_7 \end{bmatrix}
= \frac{1}{8}
\begin{bmatrix}
\uparrow & \uparrow & \uparrow & \uparrow & \uparrow & \uparrow & \uparrow & \uparrow \\
\uparrow & \nearrow & \rightarrow & \searrow & \downarrow & \swarrow & \leftarrow & \nwarrow \\
\uparrow & \rightarrow & \downarrow & \leftarrow & \uparrow & \rightarrow & \downarrow & \leftarrow \\
\uparrow & \searrow & \leftarrow & \nearrow & \downarrow & \nwarrow & \rightarrow & \swarrow \\
\uparrow & \downarrow & \uparrow & \downarrow & \uparrow & \downarrow & \uparrow & \downarrow \\
\uparrow & \swarrow & \rightarrow & \nwarrow & \downarrow & \nearrow & \leftarrow & \searrow \\
\uparrow & \leftarrow & \downarrow & \rightarrow & \uparrow & \leftarrow & \downarrow & \rightarrow \\
\uparrow & \nwarrow & \leftarrow & \swarrow & \downarrow & \searrow & \rightarrow & \nearrow
\end{bmatrix}
\begin{bmatrix} g_0 \\ g_1 \\ g_2 \\ g_3 \\ g_4 \\ g_5 \\ g_6 \\ g_7 \end{bmatrix}
\qquad (2.20a)
$$

Each element in the square matrix represents a unit vector $e^{-j2\pi kn/N}$ with a certain angular orientation, and multiplication by this vector results in a rotation through the angle depicted. Each row in the matrix represents a different value of frequency ($k = 0, 1, 2 \ldots 7$) while each column represents a different point in time ($n = 0, 1, 2 \ldots \ldots 7$).

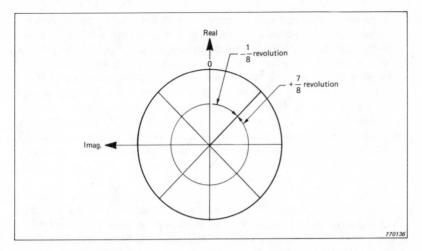

Fig.2.7. Equivalence of positive and negative rotations for sampled functions

For either k or n equal zero the angle is always zero and thus multiplication is by unity. The first row of the matrix (k = 0) represents zero frequency, and since all elements equal one, calculation of G_o involves a simple addition of all the time samples (g_n) followed by division by 8 (=N). As would be expected this results in the DC component. The second row (k = 1) represents the lowest non-zero frequency and it can be seen that for increasing values of n the angle changes by $2\pi/N$ i.e. $1/N$ th of a revolution. (Note that for the forward transform the negative sign of the exponent actually gives a rotation in the negative direction as explained previously). For k = 2 the rotational frequency is $2/N$ths of a revolution per time sample and so on up to the last row which represents $(N-1)/N$ (in this case 7/8) revolution per time sample. Note that this can be more easily interpreted as a rotation, in the opposite direction, of $1/N$ revolution per time sample and thus equally well represents the frequency $-2\pi/N$ per time sample (Fig.2.7). In fact all the frequencies above k = $N/2$ (in this case 4) are more easily interpreted as negative frequencies and this is perhaps the easiest way of understanding Shannon's Sampling Theorem.●. We have seen (Equation (2.12)) that the negative frequency components of a real-valued time function are determined with respect to the positive frequency components and thus if there were any frequency components above the Nyquist fre-

---

● Shannon's Sampling Theorem states that a sampled time signal must not contain components at frequencies above half the sampling rate (the so-called Nyquist frequency)

quency (half the sampling frequency i. e. half a revolution per time sample) then these would become inextricably mixed with the required negative frequency components, thus introducing an error. The periodicity of the spectrum for sampled time functions also becomes clear from examination of Equation (2.20a). The first row of **A** could equally well represent the sampling frequency f_s (one revolution per time sample) or $2f_s$, and so on, and thus the **A** matrix could equally represent the frequencies $k = 8$ to 15, 16 to 23 etc. (Fig.2.8). Since the rotating vectors are only sampled at discrete points in time, all information is lost about how many complete revolutions may occur between samples. However, restriction of frequency content to less than half the sampling frequency removes the ambiguity.

The misinterpretation of high frequencies (above half the sampling frequency) as lower frequencies, as illustrated in Fig.2.8, is termed "aliasing", and this is obviously one of the pitfalls to be avoided when digitizing continuous signals. It may help in understanding aliasing, to consider two practical cases with which most people are familiar.

(1) The cartwheels in western films often appear to run backwards (i. e. negative frequency) or too slowly forwards because of the sampling involved in filming.

(2) The stroboscope is in fact an aliasing device which is designed to represent high frequencies as low ones (even zero frequency when the picture is frozen).

2.2.5. Spectral Density

Despite the similarity between the various forms of the Fourier transform, it is important at the same time to point out the differences between them. For example, with those forms where the spectrum is a continuous function of frequency (Equations (2.14), (2.16)) the spectral components have the dimensions of "spectral density". In particular, the amplitude squared spectrum typically has the units of energy per unit frequency (e. g. Volt^2 seconds/Hz) and must be integrated over a finite bandwidth to give a finite energy. The term "power spectral density" (PSD) is used for stationary random functions, whose spectrum is continuous, but which have a finite and (statistically) constant power. To apply this concept to stationary deterministic signals (with discrete spectra) involves the use of delta functions as described in Section 2.1

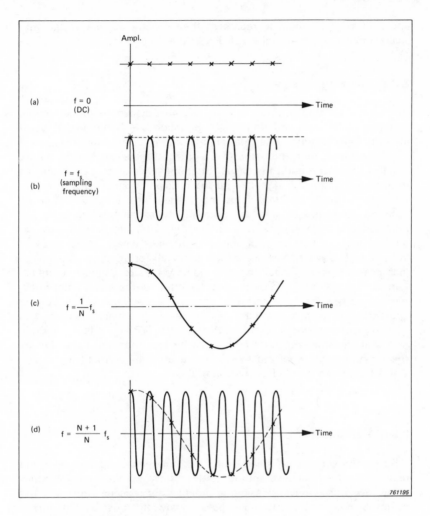

Fig.2.8. Illustration of "aliasing"
    (a) Zero frequency or DC component
    (b) Component at sampling frequency f_s interpreted as DC
    (c) Frequency component at $(1/N)f_s$
    (d) Frequency component at $[(N+1)/N]f_s$ interpreted as $(1/N)f_s$

and it is more common to represent their spectra as "power spectra" scaled directly in power units (c. f. Fig.2.5).●

2.2.6. Power vs. Energy

A further difference in dimensions becomes evident when comparing equation (2.14) with equation (2.10). Equation (2.14) is intended to apply to transients (with finite total energy) and if for example it is applied to a tone burst, then the value of the integral increases directly as the length of the tone burst increases. In contrast, equation (2.10) applies to periodic (stationary) signals, and the division by T normalises the result to a (virtually) constant value independent of the length taken into account. Consequently, the spectrum which results from squaring the amplitudes of the components obtained from Equation (2.14) has the dimensions of "energy spectral density". In cases where a PSD analyzer is used to analyze an impulse which has been recorded on a loop (tape loop or recirculating digital memory) the power spectral density units obtained must be multiplied by the loop length (i. e. repetition time) to obtain the correct results in terms of energy spectral density. If the power spectrum has been measured, then the results must also be divided by the analyzer bandwidth to obtain the spectral density. It is a precondition that the analyzer bandwidth must be less than the bandwidth of the function being analyzed for such a result to be correct (see Section 2.4.4 for a more detailed discussion of this).

2.3. BANDWIDTH

So far the concept of "bandwidth" has not been explained, since the results of a mathematical Fourier analysis have infinitely narrow bandwidth (df). This is never possible in practice, for reasons which will become obvious, and so the concept of bandwidth must be introduced.

● Strictly speaking, none of the forms of the Fourier transform shown in Fig.2.6 applies to stationary non-periodic signals, and for example it would be necessary to normalise Equation (2.14), by dividing by a factor proportional to the long-term limit of the integral (e. g. T for deterministic signals, $\sqrt{T}$ for random signals) before taking the limit as $T \to \infty$. In practice, this mathematical finesse is not necessary, because all practical signals are of finite duration and can thus be treated as transients (to which Equation (2.14) applies) even when the results are interpreted in terms of the equivalent infinitely long signal, which is a mathematical abstraction. The various signal types mentioned here are discussed in detail in Section 2.4.

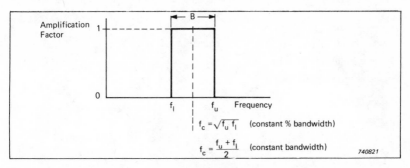

Fig.2.9. Ideal filter

The term originates from the use of bandpass filters, which have the property of passing only that part of the total power whose frequency lies within a finite range (the bandwidth). The concept can be understood from consideration of the so-called "ideal filter" whose power transmission characteristics are illustrated in Fig.2.9. This transmits, at full power, all components lying within its passband of width B and attenuates completely all components at other frequencies.

The concept of bandwidth can also be extended to mean the degree of frequency uncertainty associated with a measurement. This applies directly to the case of the ideal filter, in the sense that the frequency of a transmitted component can only be said to lie somewhere in the bandwidth. Practical filters have a characteristic which differs from that of an ideal filter as illustrated in Fig.2.10. These differences are discussed in more detail in the next chapter, but at this stage it is useful to consider the meaning of bandwidth in this case, since it is no longer immediately obvious. The so-called "effective noise bandwidth" is defined as being the width of ideal filter with the same reference transmission level which transmits the same power from a white noise source (which has a PSD which is constant with frequency). It can be obtained by integrating the area under the power transmission curve (the shaded area in Fig.2.10) and dividing by the reference level.

The bandwidth associated with a measurement is not necessarily determined by the bandwidth of the filter used (in particular where none is used such as in digital calculations). The other factor which plays a role is the effective length of record on which the measurement is made, and in fact a record length of T limits the bandwidth to a minimum of $1/T$.

This simple relationship may be demonstrated from the following

23

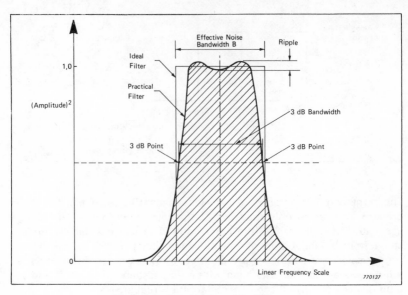

Fig.2.10. Practical vs. ideal filter

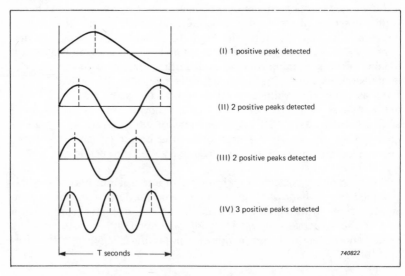

Fig.2.11. Measurement of frequency by counting peaks

24

model: suppose that it is necessary to measure the frequency of an un-
known sine-like wave, and that the duration of the measurement is
fixed at T seconds. With what bandwidth can the measurement be
made? One way of making the measurement is to count the number of
positive peaks of the sine wave and divide the number by T. This
method is illustrated in Fig.2.11.

Let us now examine which frequencies are measured for the examples of Fig.2.11. In case (I), one peak is counted, and hence the frequency is $1/T$ Hz. In cases (II) and (III), 2 peaks are detected, and hence
the frequency of both is $2/T$ Hz. In case (IV), 3 peaks give a frequency
of $3/T$ Hz. Hence, because we have limited the measurement period to
T seconds, it is not possible to measure a sine wave frequency to better
than $1/T$, i. e. the best bandwidth which can be obtained is $1/T$ Hz.

It might be argued that the frequency could be measured more accurately by extrapolating the sinewave to an integer number of periods

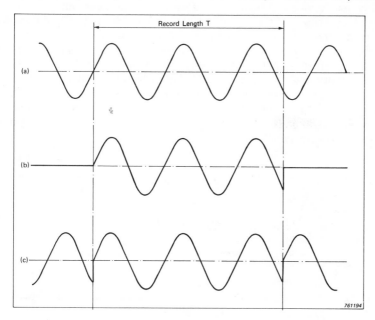

Fig.2.12. Three possibilities for the signal of Fig.2.11(IV)
(a) Continuous sine wave
(b) Tone-burst of length T
(c) Loop of length T

and measuring this time exactly, but it must not be forgotten that it is not certain that the signal continues as a sinewave. Two other possibilities are illustrated in Fig.2.12 for the signal of Fig.2.11 (IV). In one case the signal is a tone burst of length T, while in the other case it is a periodic signal of length T. Even though these have different spectra, they have in common that their bandwidth is less than or equal to $1/T$ as will be seen later. Thus the frequency uncertainty, or bandwidth, is equal to $1/T$.

The concept of a filter characteristic being associated with a record length of T can also be illustrated using the rotating vector analogy introduced previously. The discussion of periodic signals in Section 2.2.1 considered only the case where the frequency components all fell at multiples of f_1 the fundamental frequency. Even after multiplication by $e^{-j2\pi f_k t}$, the rotation of any component would still be at an integer multiple of f_1 and would thus result in an integral number of rotations over the period time T. As illustrated in Fig.2.3(b) this would always result in an integration to zero for components other than that with frequency f_k. If the signal contained a continuous range of frequencies, however, then the integration of the rotating vector over time T would not always be exactly zero. For example, if there is a component with a frequency of $f_k + \Delta f$, then after multiplication by $e^{-j2\pi f_k t}$, it will continue to rotate at Δf. If Δf is only a small percentage of f_1 , then the total rotation over time T would only be a small part of a revolution, and the average would still be almost the same as with zero rotation (see Fig.2.13(a)). Note, however, that the phase of the resultant is turned through a small angle.

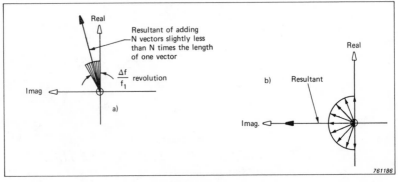

Fig.2.13. (a) Resultant for $\Delta f \ll f_1$
(b) Resultant for $\Delta f = f_1/2$

26

When $\Delta f = f_1/2$ (i.e. the frequency lies halfway between f_k and f_{k+1}) then the vector will rotate through half a revolution in time T and the resultant is illustrated in Fig.2.13(b).

The length of the resultant can be determined by integrating that component of each vector which is aligned with the resultant and in Appendix A it is shown how this results in:

$$A_{\text{result}} = \frac{2}{\pi} A \qquad (2.21)$$

This is approximately $3,9\,\text{dB}$ less than A. In this case, the phase of the resultant is obviously turned through $90°$.

Continuing on in the same way, one finds that the resultant at $\Delta f = f_1$ is of course zero, but for example with $\Delta f = 1,5\,f_1$ the situation is as illustrated in three dimensions in Fig.2.14 (where the axis normal to the complex plane now represents time rather than frequency).

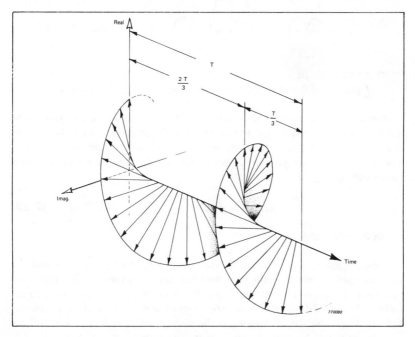

Fig.2.14. Effect of $\Delta f = 3f_1/2$

In this case, the vector rotates through 1,5 revolutions in time T, where the resultant of the first revolution is zero and only the last half revolution gives a resultant. The length of the resultant will now evidently be 1/3 of that for $\Delta f = f_1/2$ (since only 1/3 of the total number of vectors contribute to it).

$$\text{i.e. } A_{\text{result}} = \frac{2}{3\pi} \, A \quad \text{(approx. 13,4 dB less than } A) \quad (2.22)$$

If the relative amplitude of the resultant is plotted against Δf it will in fact be found to trace the well-known $|sin\,x/x|$ curve as illustrated in Fig.2.15.

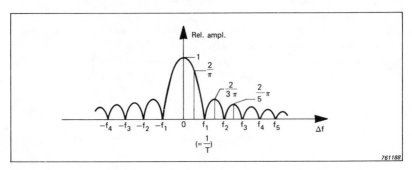

Fig.2.15. Effective "filter characteristic" for record length T

This can be considered as a filter characteristic with which the original signal is filtered when the record length is limited to T. Note that the power transmission characteristic is thus equal to $sin^2 x/x^2$ (where $x = \pi\,\Delta f/f$) and as shown in Appendix A this has an effective noise bandwidth given by

$$B_{\text{eff}} = \frac{1}{T} \quad (2.23)$$

as previously stated.

Before leaving this analogy it is worth noting that the phase shift of the resultant is due to the fact that the time signal was not taken as symmetrical about zero time. If the integration period is chosen to be from $-T/2$ to $T/2$ and the original signal symmetrical (i. e. a cosine) the resultant will in all cases be directed along the Real Axis and no phase shift will be introduced. This is illustrated for the case of $\Delta f = f_1/2$ in Fig.2.16, which should thus be compared with Fig.2.13(b).

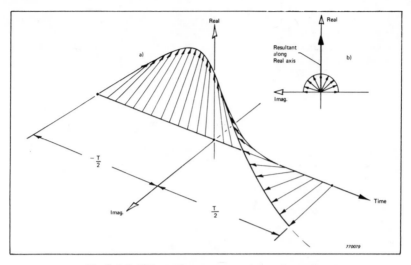

Fig.2.16. Effect of symmetry about time zero
(a) 3-dimensional representation
(b) View along time axis

Quite a lot of space has been devoted to these fundamental relationships between record length (or "time window") and the resulting spectrum. The results can be obtained much more efficiently using the "Convolution Theorem" of Section 2.5.3, but it is thought that this elementary approach gives more physical insight, and helps in the interpretation of convolution.

2.4. SIGNAL TYPES

Before discussing convolution it is as well to examine the various types of signal which are encountered in practice. The type of signal to be analyzed has an influence on the type of analysis to be carried out and also on the choice of analysis parameters. Fig.2.17 indicates the basic divisions into different signal types.

The most fundamental division is into stationary and non-stationary signals. A rigorous definition of stationary random functions is given in Ref.2.2, but for practical purposes it is sufficient to interpret stationary functions as being those whose average properties do not vary with time and are thus independent of the particular sample record used to determine them. This applies to both deterministic and random signals,

29

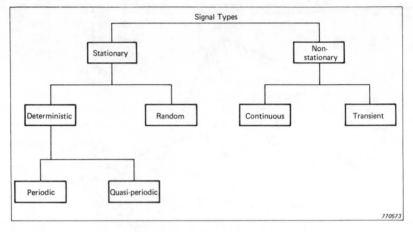

Fig.2.17. Division into different signal types

but in particular in the latter case it is important to realise that the results obtained from different records are not necessarily identical, just
equally valid.

The instantaneous value of a stationary deterministic signal is predic-
table at all points in time, while with stationary random signals it is
only the statistical properties such as mean values, variances etc.,
which are known.

Non-stationary signals may be roughly divided into continuous non-
stationary signals (of which a good example is speech) and transient signals which may be defined as those which start and finish at zero. Of
course in practice even signals such as speech must start and finish at
some time, but the difference is perhaps more fundamentally that a
transient is treated and analyzed as a whole, whereas a continuous non-
stationary signal, such as speech, will normally be analyzed in short
sections, each of which will often be quasi-stationary.

It is interesting to look at each of these signal types in more detail, so
as to see how the differences show up in various representations.

2.4.1. Stationary Deterministic Signals

Stationary deterministic signals are made up entirely of sinusoidal
components at discrete frequencies. In periodic signals, as we have

seen, all these discrete frequencies are multiples of some fundamental frequency, the reciprocal of the periodic time. In quasi-periodic signals, the frequencies of the various sinusoids are not harmonically related. If carried to extremes, this means that the ratio between at least two frequencies must be an irrational number such as $\sqrt{2}$, but in practice it can be seen that quasi-periodic signals will typically arise from mixtures of two or more independent sets of harmonics, such as from an aircraft turbine engine with two independently rotating shafts.

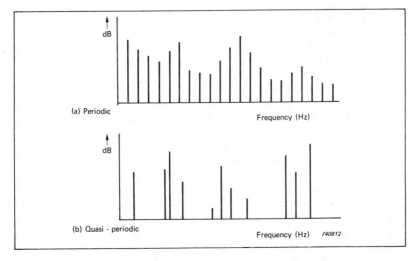

Fig.2.18. Typical periodic and quasi-periodic spectra

Fig.2.18(a) and (b) shows how the power spectra of typical periodic and quasi-periodic signals appear. The approach to frequency analyzing them is basically the same. The filter bandwidth should be selected so as to separate the most closely spaced components and in that case there will only be one sinusoid in the filter passband at one time. If this condition is satisfied, the transmitted power is independent of the bandwidth. It might be argued that the closest spacing will only be known after analysis, and in some cases it may be necessary to use a sort of trial-and-error process, but in many cases the likely location of frequency components will be known in advance, e. g. as harmonics of a machine rotational speed, or mains frequency.

Normally, a constant bandwidth analysis on a linear frequency scale will be most appropriate to the analysis of deterministic signals, since harmonically related components will then be equally separated and resolved.

31

Occasionally, it is not possible to separate closely spaced components, and then it is important to realise that the signal passed by the filter will have a beat frequency equal to the difference between the most closely spaced components. The signal must then be analyzed over several periods of the beat frequency in order to be considered as stationary. This will occasionally be a more demanding requirement than that required in the analysis of random signals.

2.4.2. Stationary Random Signals

In contrast to deterministic signals, random signals have a spectrum which is continuously distributed with frequency, as shown in Fig.2.19. Accordingly, the power transmitted by a filter varies with the bandwidth, and for a relatively flat spectrum is directly proportional to it. As mentioned in Section 2.2.5 it is possible to remove this influence of filter bandwidth by dividing the transmitted power by the bandwidth, thus normalising the result to a "power spectral density". The requirement that the spectrum is relatively flat will be satisfied if the filter bandwidth is chosen to be narrower (e. g. one-third of the width) of any peaks in the spectrum being measured. Once again a trial-and-error process may sometimes be required to determine whether this condition is satisfied, but in many cases it will be known in advance from the physical conditions. For example, peaks in the spectra of random signals often arise from filtration of a broadband signal by a physical system whose frequency response is characterised by a number of resonances, each with a certain Q-factor (i. e. amplification factor). The

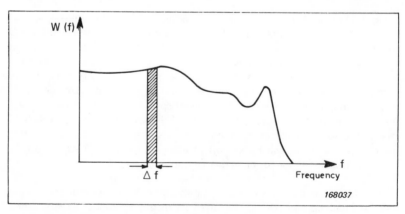

Fig.2.19. Continuous spectrum of a stationary random signal

range of Q-factors will often be determined by choice of materials etc., and since there is an inverse relationship between Q-factor and percentage bandwidth, the latter will often be known roughly in advance.

Even though the power spectrum of a random function may be well-defined, the phase spectrum is random, and thus normally not of interest in the analysis of single signals. In the analysis of multiple channel signals the phase relationships between two or more spectra will often be meaningful.

Even though their instantaneous value cannot be predicted, random signals may be characterised by their probability density curves. The meaning of this concept can be understood by reference to Fig.2.20. The probability density $p(x)$ at some level x is defined as the probability that the signal value lies between x and $x + \Delta x$, divided by the interval width Δx (thus giving a density). Thus if $P(x)$ represents the total probability that the signal value is less than x, then

$$p(x) = \lim_{\Delta x \to 0} \frac{P(x + \Delta x) - P(x)}{\Delta x} \qquad (2.24)$$

Referring to Fig.2.20, it will be seen that

$$P(x + \Delta x) - P(x) = \lim_{T \to \infty} \frac{\Sigma \, \Delta t_n}{T} \qquad (2.25)$$

where each Δt_n represents one of the time intervals in T where the signal lies between x and $x + \Delta x$.

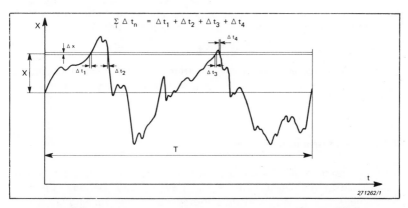

Fig.2.20. Sketch illustrating the concept of probability density

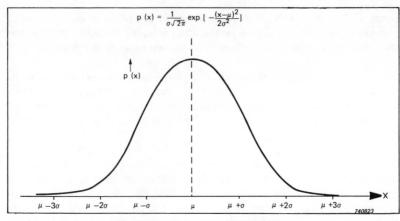

$$p(x) = \frac{1}{\sigma\sqrt{2\pi}} \exp\left[-\frac{(x-\mu)^2}{2\sigma^2}\right]$$

Fig.2.21. Gaussian distribution

Gaussian random signals, which can be used as a model for many random signals encountered in practice, have a probability density curve of Gaussian shape, as illustrated in Fig.2.21.

The equation of this curve is

$$p(x) = \frac{1}{\sigma\sqrt{2\pi}} \, exp\left\{-\frac{1}{2}\frac{(x-\mu)^2}{\sigma^2}\right\} \qquad (2.26)$$

This may appear somewhat formidable, but it is in fact just an e^{-x^2} curve centred on the mean value μ and scaled in the following way:

1. In the x-direction it is scaled in terms of σ, the standard deviation from the mean μ. For zero mean, σ is also the RMS level of the signal, and σ^2 the variance or power.

2. In the y-direction it is scaled so that the total integral under the curve for all x is 1, which of course is the probability that x can have any value between $\pm\infty$.

2.4.3. Pseudo-random Signals

Pseudo-random signals are a particular type of periodic signal sometimes used to simulate random signals. Even though periodic, the periodic time T is very long and thus the spectrum line spacing ($1/T$) very close (Fig.2.22). Phase relationships between adjacent spectral lines

34

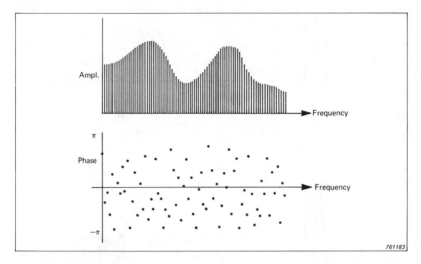

Fig.2.22. Amplitude and phase spectra for a pseudo-random signal

are to all intents and purposes random, so that provided the bandwidth of any resonance peaks spans over a large number of spectral lines then the effect of applying it as input to a physical system will be very similar to that of a truly random signal. The probability density of such pseudo-random signals may be made very close to Gaussian.

On the other hand, a pseudo-random signal can be reproduced exactly, and this may be of benefit in the standardisation of testing.

2.4.4. Transient Signals

As mentioned previously, a transient may be considered as a signal which commences and finishes at zero. Fig.2.23 shows the following three typical examples:

1. A rectangular pulse
2. A half cosine pulse
3. A tone burst

together with their spectra as derived using equation (2.14). It is emphasized that the squares of these spectrum amplitudes have units of **energy** spectral density, as explained in Section 2.2.6. Thus the inte-

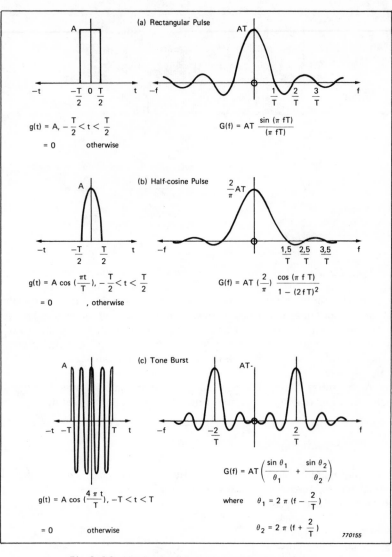

(a) Rectangular Pulse

$$g(t) = A, \quad -\frac{T}{2} < t < \frac{T}{2}$$
$$= 0 \qquad \text{otherwise}$$

$$G(f) = AT \, \frac{\sin(\pi fT)}{(\pi fT)}$$

(b) Half-cosine Pulse

$$g(t) = A \cos\left(\frac{\pi t}{T}\right), \quad -\frac{T}{2} < t < \frac{T}{2}$$
$$= 0 \qquad , \text{otherwise}$$

$$G(f) = AT \left(\frac{2}{\pi}\right) \frac{\cos(\pi f T)}{1 - (2fT)^2}$$

(c) Tone Burst

$$g(t) = A \cos\left(\frac{4\pi t}{T}\right), \quad -T < t < T$$
$$= 0 \qquad \text{otherwise}$$

$$G(f) = AT \left(\frac{\sin \theta_1}{\theta_1} + \frac{\sin \theta_2}{\theta_2}\right)$$

$$\text{where} \quad \theta_1 = 2\pi\left(f - \frac{2}{T}\right)$$
$$\theta_2 = 2\pi\left(f + \frac{2}{T}\right)$$

770155

Fig.2.23. Various transients and their spectra
(a) Rectangular pulse
(b) Half cosine pulse
(c) Tone-burst

36

gral of the squared spectrum amplitude over all frequency gives the total energy of the transient. This can also be obtained by integrating the instantaneous power (i. e. amplitude squared) over all time.

i. e. $$\int_{-\infty}^{\infty} |G(f)|^2 \, df = \int_{-\infty}^{\infty} |g(t)|^2 \, dt \qquad (2.27)$$

This is a more general form of Parseval's theorem which was referred to in Section 2.2.1 (See also Ref. 2.1).

All the above examples are real even functions which transform to real even functions in the other domain. In the more general case, description of the overall spectrum requires that the phase spectrum be shown as well. As an example, Fig.2.24 shows the amplitude and phase spectra for a rectangular pulse starting at zero time, and this can be compared with Fig.2.23(a).

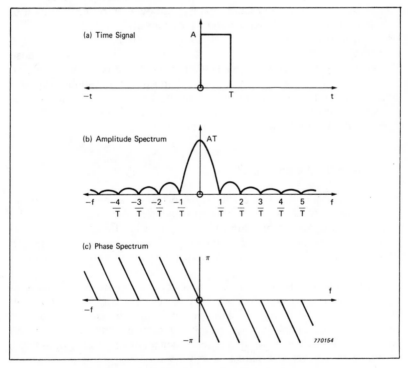

Fig.2.24. Rectangular pulse starting from zero

37

Analysis of a transient is usually performed by treating it either directly or implicitly as though it were repeated periodically with repetition time T. Because of the artificially introduced periodicity, the measured spectrum becomes a line spectrum with line spacing $1/T$, but the individual lines can be considered as samples of the true continuous spectrum, (see Section 2.5.3) and the line spacing can be made arbitrarily small by increasing T.

Of course the spectrum of the periodic signal will normally be represented on an amplitude rather than a spectral density scale, but the scaling of the results is relatively simple. The measured power of each spectral line is the average power of the periodic signal in a frequency bandwidth corresponding to the line spacing. The energy in the same frequency bandwidth for one repetition of the transient is evidently obtained by multiplying this mean power by the repetition time T. Finally, the energy spectral density at each frequency is obtained by dividing by the bandwidth $1/T$, so that the overall result is a multiplication by T^2. It should be noted that the result obtained will even so be independent of T (provided the latter is longer than the transient) since for example a doubling of the repetition time will result in a quartering (-6 dB) of the measured power of a spectral line at a given frequency, partly because the same energy is spread over twice the time, and partly because one spectral line is replaced by two. A doubling of the repetition time will however permit measurement with half the bandwidth, and thus allow a more detailed resolution of the spectrum. This, and other practical considerations are discussed in more detail in Section 3.7.

2.4.5. Non-Stationary Signals

Although the term "non-stationary" covers all signals which do not satisfy the requirements for stationary signals, the majority of useful non-stationary signals are such that they can be divided up into short quasi-stationary sections. For example, a continuous train of speech can be divided up into short individual sounds; vowels, consonants etc.

The process of dividing up such a continuous signal into short sections is called "time windowing" because the total signal can be considered to be viewed through a window which only transmits the portion of interest. The simplest way of applying such a window is to cut off the signal at each end. It will be seen that this can be considered as a multiplication by a rectangular weighting function of length T, which gives uniform weighting along the selected sample. However, the effect of this on a typical frequency spectrum component was discussed in Section 2.3 where it was shown that the original spectrum has effectively been filtered by a filter characteristic corresponding to the Fourier transform of the rectangular weighting fuction. In the Section 3.6 it is shown that smooth non-uniform weighting functions, such as the Gaussian curve, have a more desirable filtering effect and are often preferable, and details are given as to their selection. Fig.2.25 shows how such a Gaussian "window" can be moved along a speech record to permit successive analysis of the various components of a particular utterance. After multiplication of the original signal by such a weighting curve, the result is a transient which may be analyzed in the same way as transients in general. The question of scaling is, however, the reverse of that discussed in Section 2.4.4, since results will normally be interpreted in terms of the power of the equivalent stationary signal represented by the windowed segment. Details of this are given in the appropriate sections on practical analysis.

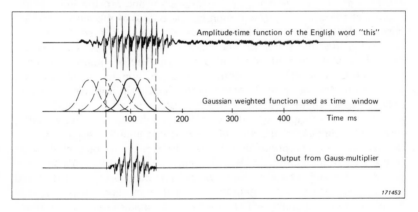

Fig.2.25. Use of a gaussian window in speech analysis

2.5. CONVOLUTION

It was mentioned in the Introduction that one of the most important properties of the Fourier Transform is that it transforms a convolution into a multiplication. It is the intention here to examine this statement in more detail, and at the same time to point out the advantages which accrue from it, as well as using the theorem to give a better theoretical background to some of the statements made in earlier sections.

First, it is necessary to define convolution and also to give examples of its application so that it acquires a physical meaning.

The convolution of two time functions $f(t)$ and $h(t)$ is defined mathematically as:

$$g(t) = \int_{-\infty}^{\infty} f(\tau)h(t - \tau) \, d\tau \qquad (2.28)$$

For convenience, this is often represented symbolically as:

$$g(t) = f(t) * h(t) \qquad (2.28(a)$$

where the star means "convolved with".

One major application of this relationship is to the case where $f(t)$ represents an input signal to a physical system and $h(t)$ the impulse response of the system. $g(t)$ will then be the output of the system. A discussion of Fig.2.26 should help to illustrate why this is so. Fig.2.26(a) represents the time signal $f(t)$ and Fig.2.26(b) the impulse response $h(t)$ of a physical system to which it is applied. The assumption is made that each point in $f(t)$ can be considered as an impulse (delta function) weighted by the value of $f(t)$ at that point. Each such impulse excites an impulse response, the scaling of which is proportional to the level of $f(t)$ and whose time origin coincides with the impulse. The output signal at time t, $g(t)$, consists of the sum of these scaled impulse responses each delayed by the appropriate time interval from the time of excitation up to the time of measurement. Because each point on the response curve consists of a sum of components which have been excited at different times, it is necessary to integrate over a dummy time variable τ. It is simplest at first to consider $f(\tau)$ as a series of impulses at discrete times t_n (with time increment Δt) and then let Δt tend to zero in a final limiting process. Fig.2.26(a) shows a typical impulse $f(t_n)$, and in Fig.2.26(c) the impulse response from this alone is shown as a heavy line. It will be seen that this response has t_n as its origin, and for example the peak value of the response occurs at time $t_o = t_n + \tau_o$ where τ_o is depicted in Fig.2.26(b). The value of this peak is evidently $f(t_n) \cdot h(\tau_o)$, i. e. $f(t_n) \cdot h(t_o - t_n)$, and thus at any other time t the value of the response (from $f(t_n)$ alone) is equal to $f(t_n) \cdot h(t - t_n)$ as illustrated. The response at time t_o from the signal applied at time t_n might be termed $g_n(t_o)$ and thus the total response at time t_o is equal to the sum of all the responses excited at the various times.

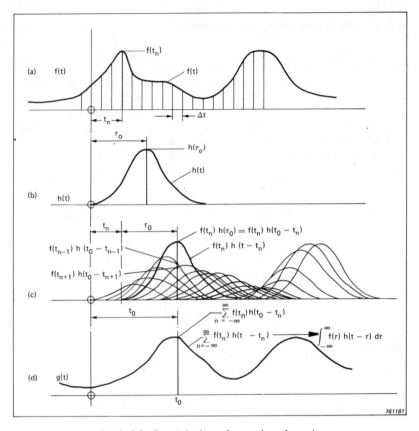

Fig.2.26. Convolution of two time functions

i.e. $\quad g(t_0) = \sum_{n=-\infty}^{\infty} g_n(t_0) = \sum_{n=-\infty}^{\infty} f(t_n)h(t_0 - t_n)$

More generally, at time t the response

$$g(t) = \sum_{n=-\infty}^{\infty} f(t_n)h(t - t_n) \qquad (2.29)$$

It will be seen that in the limit as $\Delta t \to 0$ Equation (2.29) tends to Equation (2.28) as shown in Fig.2.26(d).

2.5.1. Convolution with a Delta Function

A special case which arises in various situations involves convolution with a delta function, which in fact is found to be relatively simple. Fig.2.27, which is comparable with Fig.2.26, illustrates a typical situation where $h(t)$ is a unit delta function $\delta(t - \tau_o)$ with a delay time of τ_o (Fig.2.27(b)). In Fig.2.27(c) it is shown how each discrete impulse in the original time function $f(t_n)$ now generates a single impulse in the response, delayed by τ_o. The overall effect is to delay the whole signal by τ_o, but otherwise to leave it unchanged. If the delta function is weighted with a scaling factor then the entire response is also weighted by that scaling factor.

In general it can be said that the effect of convolving a function with a delta function is to shift its origin to the delta function.

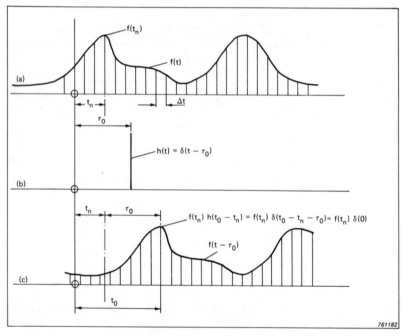

Fig.2.27. Convolution with a delta function

42

2.5.2. Convolution of Spectral Functions

So far only the convolution of two real-valued functions has been discussed, but it is possible for two complex functions to be convolved, for example two frequency spectra.

The convolution equation is still the same, viz.

$$F(f) * H(f) = \int_{-\infty}^{\infty} F(\phi)H(f - \phi) \, d\phi \qquad (2.30)$$

but since $F(f)$ and $H(f)$ are complex variables, the multiplication is now a complex multiplication (i. e. multiplication of amplitudes and addition of phases) and the integration represents a complex or vector addition.

2.5.3. Convolution Theorem

The Convolution Theorem states that a Fourier Transform (either forward or inverse) transforms a convolution into a multiplication and vice versa. For example, for the case represented by Equation (2.28)

if $G(f) = \mathscr{F}\{g(t)\}$ i. e. the forward Fourier transform of $g(t)$

$F(f) = \mathscr{F}\{f(t)\}$

and $H(f) = \mathscr{F}\{h(t)\}$ $\qquad\qquad$ (2.31)

and if $g(t) = f(t) * h(t)$

then $G(f) = F(f) \cdot H(f)$

A proof of this is given in Appendix A for a forward Fourier transform, but it can be appreciated that because of the symmetry of equations (2.14) and (2.15) the same will apply to the inverse transform.

The benefits of this are immediately apparent when interpreted in terms of the excitation and response of a physical system. $H(f)$, the forward Fourier transform of the impulse response is known as the frequency response or transfer function. The spectrum of the output is obtained very simply by multiplying the input spectrum by the transfer function at each frequency. The equivalent convolution in the time domain is evidently a much more complicated procedure.

Another example of a convolution transforming to a product is represented by the case referred to in Section 2.4.4, viz. that periodic repetition of a transient results in a sampling of its spectrum in the frequency domain. This is illustrated in Fig.2.28. Fig.2.28(a) shows the original transient and its spectrum. Fig.2.28(b) shows a train of unit impulses with a spacing of T, and its spectrum which is another train of impulses with spacing $1/T$ (Ref. 2.1, 2.3). Fig.2.28(c) shows the periodically repeated transient which can be considered as the convolution of the original transient with the impulse train (see Section 2.5.1). The Convolution Theorem indicates that the result of this convolution will be a multiplication of the respective spectra, thus giving a train of delta functions at frequency intervals of $1/T$ and weighted by the original spectrum level at the corresponding frequency. This corresponds to a sampling of the spectrum at intervals of $1/T$ as assumed in Section 2.4.4.

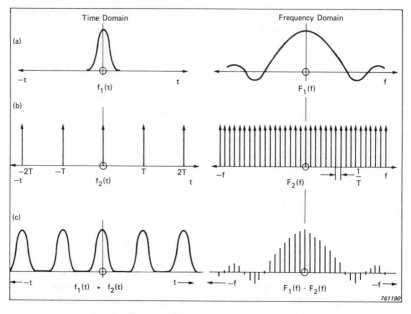

Fig.2.28. Periodic repetition of an impulse

It is perhaps also useful to give an example of the other version of the Convolution Theorem viz. that a multiplication in the time domain transforms to a convolution in the frequency domain.

Fig.2.29 illustrates the case discussed in Section 2.3, viz. the effect

44

of a truncation to a record length of T. Fig.2.29(a) represents an endless cosine function in both time and frequency domains. Note that the arrows at $\pm f_o$ represent delta functions which should of course be infinitely high. For comparison purposes Fig.2.29(b) shows a sine function, whose spectrum only differs by virtue of the initial phase angles of the positive and negative frequency components. Fig.2.29(c) shows a rectangular "time window" of length T, evenly divided about zero time, and its frequency spectrum. As shown in Appendix A the latter is a ($sin\ x/x$) function with zeroes at multiples of $1/T$. The third column of Fig.2.29 shows the power spectrum which is to be discussed later.

Restricting the length of either the cosine or sine function to T is the same as multiplying it by the rectangular time window and this is illustrated in Fig.2.29(d) and (e). This corresponds in the frequency domain to a convolution of the respective frequency spectra. This can be done separately for the positive and negative frequency delta functions, and consists, as shown previously, in replacing each of them by the convolving function $F_3(f)$. The result is then obtained as the sum of the positive and negative frequency contributions. It will be appreciated that it is only in the vicinity of zero frequency (where the two ($sin\ x/x$) functions have the same magnitude) that there is a significant interaction. In the vicinity of either f_o or $-f_o$ the result is virtually a ($sin\ x/x$) filter characteristic centred on $\pm f_o$, as derived heuristically in Section 2.3. In the vicinity of zero frequency it is perhaps of interest to note that because the two ($sin\ x/x$) functions have the same phase in Fig.2.29(d), they reinforce and give a DC component, while in Fig.2.29(e) they are opposed and give zero DC component. This can also be seen from the respective time functions, where in Fig.2.29(d) it has 5 positive lobes against 4 negative, while that in Fig.2.29(e) has $4\frac{1}{2}$ positive and negative lobes and is thus balanced.

It is interesting to investigate what effect the convolution of the complex spectra has on the power spectra, since, as mentioned previously, one is often most interested in the power spectrum. The third column of Fig.2.29 shows the power spectra corresponding to the various complex spectra, and this reveals that although the power spectra for the sine and cosine are the same (Fig.2.29(a) and (b)) the power spectra for the convolved spectra are different (Fig.2.29(d) and (e)). Thus, the power spectrum of the convolved function is not equal to the convolution of the power spectra. However, Fig.2.30 compares the latter with the two other alternatives, and it is found that it lies between them, and in any case it is only in the vicinity of zero frequency that there is any appreciable difference. The convolution of the two power spectra

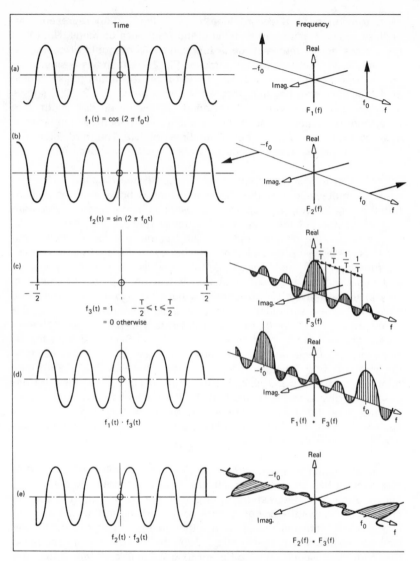

Fig.2.29. Restriction of sinusoidal signals to a length of T

has a value at zero frequency which is double the PSD of the contribution of the positive frequency component alone (i. e. + 3 dB). The power spectrum of the cosine case (Fig.2.29(a)) is four times larger at zero frequency (i.e. + 6 dB) since the linear amplitudes add rather than the

46

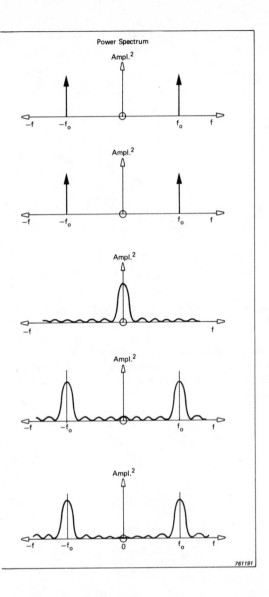

squared amplitudes. The convolution of the power spectra in fact repres-ents the "average" case, where the phase angle between the positive and negative frequency components of the sinusoid is 90°, and this is incidentally the value which will be approached if the power spectrum

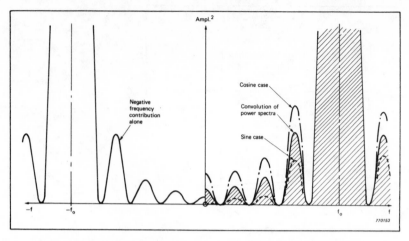

Fig.2.30. Detail of power spectra in the vicinity of zero frequency

is obtained by averaging over several records of length T taken at random along the sinusoid.

Thus in this sense it can be said that the power spectrum of the convolution is equal to the convolution of the power spectra, and this point is pursued further in Section 3.5.3 where the subject of time windowing is treated in more detail.

3. ANALOG ANALYSIS

The classical method of obtaining the frequency spectrum of an electrical signal is to pass it through a number of analog filters with different centre frequencies (or one filter whose centre frequency is moved
over a frequency range) and measure the transmitted power at each frequency.

With the filter fixed at one centre frequency, its output will be the result of convolving the input signal with the filter impulse response. In
the frequency domain this corresponds to a multiplication of the two
(complex) frequency functions. Thus the transmitted signal will have
an amplitude spectrum equal to the product of the two individual
amplitude spectra and consequently a power spectrum (i. e. amplitude
squared) equal to the product of the two power spectra (Fig.3.1). At the

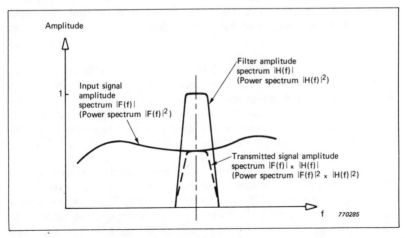

Fig.3.1. Amplitude and power spectra for a filtered signal

same time the phase relationships of the various signal components will be modified by the filter, but this has no influence on the transmitted power.

Fig.3.2 shows a typical analyzer system in simple block diagram form. In order to obtain a complete spectrum the filter centre frequency must be stepped or swept over the frequency range of interest, and the rate at which this can be done is determined by the delays which arise in each of the major components, viz. filter, detector and recorder. Accordingly, each of these will be considered in detail, including a discussion of any practical details which can influence the results.

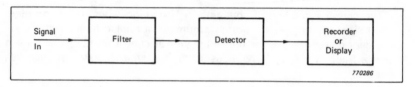

Fig.3.2. Block diagram for a basic analog analyzer system

3.1. FILTERS

A basic choice to be made is between constant absolute bandwidth and constant relative (percentage) bandwidth where the absolute bandwidth is a fixed percentage of the tuned centre frequency. Fig.3.3 compares these two alternatives on both linear and logarithmic frequency scales and illustrates one of the most fundamental differences between them.

Constant bandwidth gives uniform resolution on a linear frequency scale and this, for example, gives equal resolution and separation of harmonically related components and this will facilitate detection of a harmonic pattern (Fig.3.4). However, the linear frequency scale automatically gives a restriction of the useful frequency range to (at the most) two decades as is evident from Fig.3.3.

Constant percentage bandwidth, on the other hand, gives uniform resolution on a logarithmic frequency scale and thus can be used over a wide frequency range of 3 or more decades. (Fig.3.3). Another feature of constant percentage bandwidth is that it corresponds to constant Q-factor (amplification ratio of resonant peaks) (Fig.3.5). It is thus both natural and efficient to analyze spectra dominated by structural reson-

50

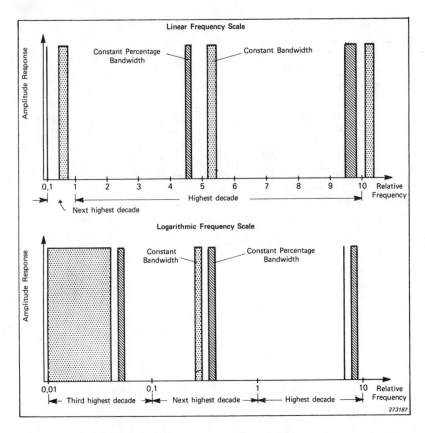

Fig.3.3. Difference between a constant bandwidth analyzer and a constant percentage bandwidth analyzer

ances on a logarithmic frequency scale with a constant percentage bandwidth somewhat narrower than the narrowest resonant peak.

Other grounds for using a logarithmic frequency scale (though not necessarily constant percentage bandwidth) are:

a) Small speed changes in, say, a machine only give a lateral displacement of the spectrum, thus simplifying direct comparison.

b) Certain relationships can most easily be seen on log-log scales such as for example, integration, which gives a change in slope of —20 dB/decade and thus means that constant velocities and dis-

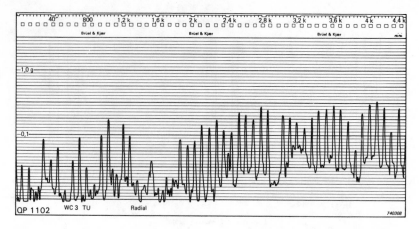

Fig.3.4. Vibration spectrum having many harmonically related components

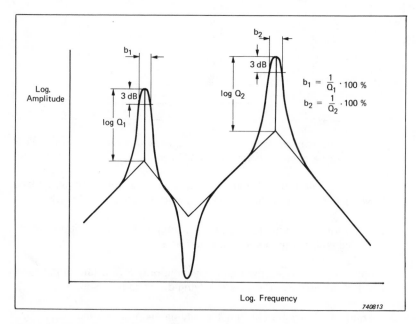

$$b_1 = \frac{1}{Q_1} \cdot 100\%$$

$$b_2 = \frac{1}{Q_2} \cdot 100\%$$

Fig.3.5. Relationship between the amplification factor Q and the relative bandwidth b

placements are represented by straight lines on an acceleration vs. frequency diagram.

It is worth paying particular attention to two special classes of constant percentage bandwidth filters, viz. octave and third octave filters since these are widely used, in particular for acoustical measurements. The former have a bandwidth such that the upper limiting frequency of the passband is always twice the lower limiting frequency, resulting in a bandwidth of 70,7%. This can be derived as follows:

If f_l = lower limiting frequency
f_u = upper limiting frequency
f_o = nominal centre frequency

Then $f_u = 2f_l$

and f_o = the geometric mean = $\sqrt{f_u \cdot f_l} = \sqrt{2f_l{}^2} = \sqrt{2}f_l$

The absolute bandwidth = $f_u - f_l = f_l$

and the relative bandwidth = $\dfrac{f_u - f_l}{f_0}$

$$= \frac{f_l}{f_0} = \frac{f_l}{\sqrt{2}f_l} = \frac{1}{\sqrt{2}} = 70,7\%$$

Internationally standardized centre frequencies for octave filters are laid down in IEC Recommendation 225 which specifies a set of contiguous filters based on a reference centre frequency of 1000 Hz.

Thus it can be seen that it is possible to cover 3 decades in frequency with 10 octave bands ranging from 22,5 Hz (lower limiting frequency for 31,5 Hz centre frequency) to 22,5 kHz (upper limiting frequency for 16 kHz centre frequency).

Third octave filters are obtained by dividing each octave band into three geometrically equal sub-sections, i. e. $f_u = 2^{1/3} f_l$ and by coincidence this is equal to one-tenth of a decade since

$$log_{10}(2^{1/3}) = 1/3 \, log_{10}(2) = 1/3 \cdot 0,3 = 0,1$$
$$= 1/10 \, log_{10}(10) = log_{10}(10^{1/10})$$

By the same procedure as for octave filters, the percentage bandwidth of third octave filters can be derived as:

$$\frac{2^{1/3} - 1}{2^{1/6}} = 23,1\%$$

3.1.1. Practical Filter Characteristic

As mentioned in Section 2.3 practical filters deviate from ideal filters in several ways as illustrated in Fig.2.10. Provided the "ripple" within the passband is kept within acceptable limits, the main characteristics of a practical filter will be its bandwidth and selectivity.

The so-called "noise bandwidth" of a filter has already been defined in Section 2.3 as the width of an ideal filter which transmits the same power from a white noise source, for the same reference transmission level in the passband. This definition is most relevant when dealing with random signals, since results derived for ideal filters are then generally applicable to practical filters with the same noise bandwidth.

Another bandwidth which can be associated with a filter is its "3 dB bandwidth" and this is simply the width of the power transmission characteristic at the "3 dB points", which as their name implies lie 3 dB below the peak amplification (Fig.2.10). It happens that this is often very close to the Noise Bandwidth and since it is much more easily measured, it is commonly used. The 3 dB bandwidth is perhaps most relevant when dealing with deterministic signals, since it gives information about how well sinusoidal components can be separated. Only filters with a relatively poor selectivity will have a 3 dB bandwidth substantially different from the noise bandwidth.

The *bandwidth* of a filter gives information as to its ability to separate components of approximately the same level. The *selectivity* indicates its ability to separate components of widely different levels. The most basic parameter indicating selectivity is known as the "Shape Factor". This is normally defined as the ratio of the width of the filter characteristic where the attenuation of the flanks is 60 dB, to its 3 dB bandwidth (Fig.3.6). In some cases, such as where the dynamic range is in any case less than 60 dB, terms such as "40 dB Shape Factor" may be used to represent the equivalent factor obtained using the breadth of the characteristic at 40 dB attenuation (Fig.3.6). Shape factor is normally used for constant bandwidth filters which have a characteristic which is symmetrical on a linear frequency scale, but it could be applied more generally.

For constant percentage bandwidth filters, however, which have a

54

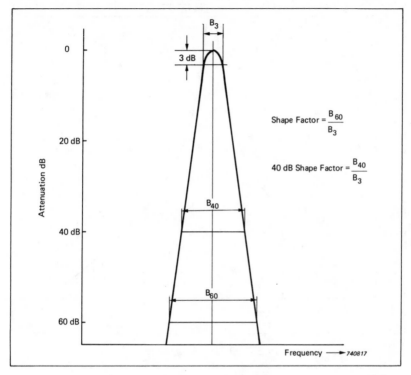

Shape Factor $= \dfrac{B_{60}}{B_3}$

40 dB Shape Factor $= \dfrac{B_{40}}{B_3}$

Fig.3.6. Shape factor

characteristic which is symmetrical on a logarithmic frequency scale, it is more common to use "Octave Selectivity", which gives the attenuation of the filter characteristic one octave on either side of the centre frequency (Fig.3.7).

3.1.2. Filter Response Time

When a signal is suddenly applied at the input of a filter, it takes some time before the latter responds. If the signal is sinusoidal and has a frequency within the passband of the filter, then the output will finally be a sinusoid of the same frequency and with the same amplitude as the original (assuming the amplitude characteristic has an amplification of 1 within the passband). The time required for the amplitude to approach its final value, however, is of the order of $1/B$ where B is the filter bandwidth.

55

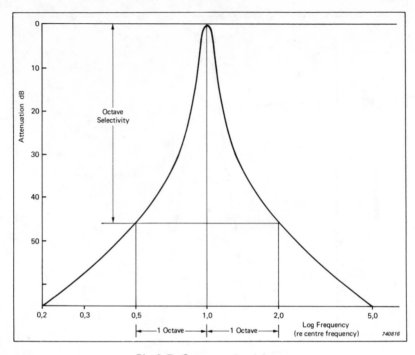

Fig.3.7. Octave selectivity

This may be expressed in the form

$$BT_R \approx 1 \qquad (3.1)$$

where T_R = filter response time●

Note that this may be modified as follows

$$\left(\frac{B}{f}\right) \cdot (fT_R) \approx 1$$

$$i.\,e.\ bn_R \approx 1 \qquad (3.2)$$

where b = relative bandwidth,

n_R = number of periods of frequency f in time T_R

e. g. for b = 1%, n_R will be approx. 100 periods, etc.

● In principle, there is a difference between the total response time for a filter and the "rise time" which is derived from Eqn. (3.1). There can be an extra delay before the filter output starts to rise, but for the majority of relevant practical filters, the difference is negligible in consideration of the fact that Eqn.(3.1) is only intended to give the order of magnitude

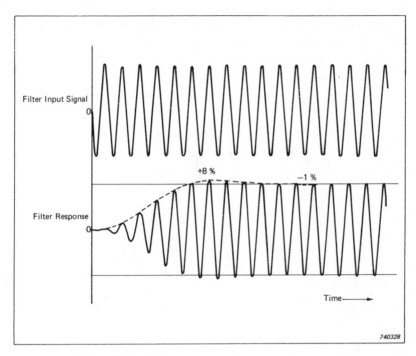

Filter Input Signal

0

Filter Response

0

+8 %

−1 %

Time

740328

Fig.3.8. Typical filter response from a 1/3 octave filter

Thus, equation (3.1) will be most applicable to constant bandwidth filters, while equation (3.2) is most applicable to constant percentage bandwidth filters.

These relationships may be thought of as another manifestation of the physical requirement that a measurement with bandwidth B requires a measurement time of at least $1/B$.

Fig.3.8 shows the response of a typical 1/3-octave filter to a suddenly applied sinusoid. Since the bandwidth is 23,1% one would expect the response time to be 4,3 periods, whereas it is seen to be actually of the order of 5 or 6 depending on the desired accuracy. This gives an idea of the order of accuracy of equations (3.1) and (3.2), although 1/3-octave filters, with their relatively steep filter characteristic, probably represent an extreme case. Another mitigating factor with swept frequency analysis is that the application of the sinusoid is not sudden, as would be the case with an ideal filter, but more gradual as the filter flank moves over the sinusoidal component (Fig.3.9). All-in-

57

all, the equations (3.1) and (3.2) give a good estimate of the delays introduced for the case of swept filtration.

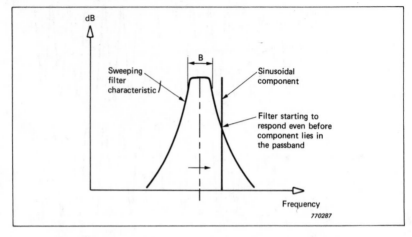

Fig.3.9. Gradual signal application with a sweeping filter

3.2. DETECTORS

When a signal has been passed through a filter the output is still in the form of an AC signal which varies continuously with time. It is necessary to measure the power of this signal to obtain the desired frequency spectrum component. This can be done mathematically by squaring the instantaneous value of the signal to obtain the instantaneous power and then integrating this over a defined time interval (the averaging time) to obtain an average value. The longer the averaging time, the smaller will be the variations in this average value, but the longer it takes to obtain the result. It is often desired to extract the square root of this mean square value to give the Root Mean Square (RMS) amplitude, since this has the same dimensions as the input signal. It also gives the practical advantage that the same output voltage range represents twice the dB range and thus gives a wider dynamic range in general.

Finally, it may be desired that the Mean Square or RMS signal be logarithmically converted to give a result in dB.

All these functions can be performed by electronic circuits known as detectors, giving a result with a high degree of accuracy with respect to the theoretical value.

3.2.1. Squaring

All high quality (so-called "true RMS") detectors square the input signal in one way or another. On the other hand, so-called "averaging detectors" perform only a rectification (as an approximation to squaring) and then average the rectified signal, but although the relationship between the "average" and "RMS" level is well-known for a sinusoidal signal, the average value for a more complex signal depends on the phase relationships between different frequency components, whereas the RMS value does not.

For many years B & K has utilised the "Wahrman" detector, named after its inventor, which achieves squaring of the (rectified) signal by means of a characteristic whereby the parabola representing the squaring relationship is approximated by a number of straight lines. Fig.3.10 illustrates a number of such parabolae for a typical detector, along with the straight lines which approximate them. The reason for the number of different parabolae is connected with square root extraction (see Section 3.2.3) and will not be gone into here; instead consideration will be limited to a single parabola which corresponds to a given RMS level. For a given parabola, it will be seen that the larger the instantaneous level of the input signal, the further out along the parabola one is working, and that beyond the last breakpoint in the approximating curve the more will be the deviation between the true squared value and the value obtained from the circuit. The ratio of peak to RMS level of a signal is known as its "crest factor", and it will be seen that the more break points there are in the approximating curve, the higher will be the crest factor which can be accommodated. As an example, 4 breakpoints give an accuracy within 1/2 dB for crest factors up to 5.

3.2.2. Averaging

The purpose of averaging is to suppress the fluctuations in the squared rectified signal from the squaring circuit, thereby obtaining an expression for the mean power, which represents the mean square spectral estimate. It should be kept in mind that Fourier analysis assumes integration over all time, which can be represented by the following equation:

$$\overline{y} = \lim_{T \to \infty} \frac{1}{T} \int_{-T/2}^{T/2} y(t)\, dt \qquad (3.3)$$

where the bar represents the average value.

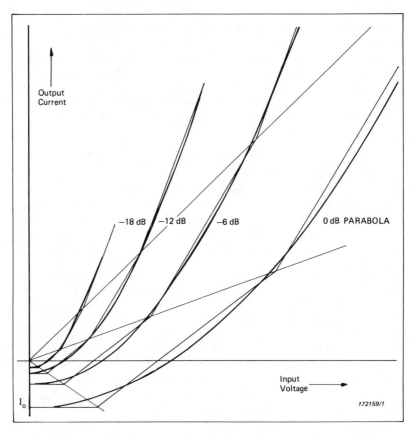

Fig.3.10. Straight-line approximations to the square-law parabolae

In practice, of course, it is necessary to limit the averaging time to a finite value, and the effect of doing this will now be examined.

The effect on equation (3.3) is to remove the limiting operation, and this results in a finite fluctuation which gets smaller as the averaging time gets longer. Suppression of the fluctuation can be considered as a lowpass filtration, and Fig.3.11 illustrates why this is so for a typical

60

sinusoidal component of frequency f_0 and amplitude A.

Fig.3.11(a) shows the original cosine signal in both time and frequency domains, while Fig.3.11(b) shows the result of squaring it. Note that the spectrum of Fig.3.11(b), while obviously corresponding to the adjacent time signal, can also be derived by convolving the spectrum of Fig.3.11(a) with itself (corresponding to the multiplication of

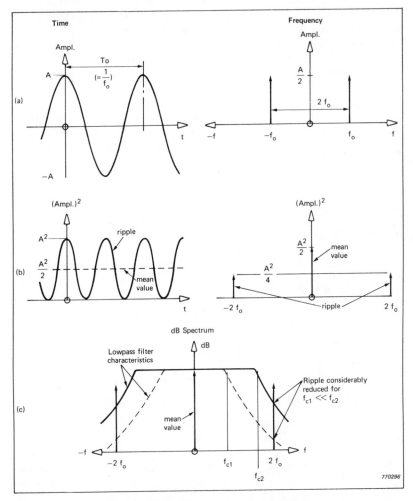

Fig.3.11. Averaging as a low-pass filtration

61

the cosine wave by itself). Thus, in the convolved spectrum there are only components when two or more delta functions from the original spectrum line up, i.e. for displacements (f in Eqn. 2.30) of 0, $+ 2f_0$ and $-2f_0$. Moreover, for displacement $f = 0$, two sets of delta functions line up so that the total component is $A^2/4 + A^2/4 = A^2/2$ whereas with $f = \pm 2f_0$, the positive frequency delta function of one spectrum lines up with the negative frequency of the other and the resulting component is thus only $A^2/4$. The true mean value is evidently the DC component in Fig.3.11(b), viz. $A^2/2$, and this can be obtained by lowpass filtering the squared signal. Fig.3.11(c) illustrates the effect of filtering with two cut-off frequencies, the lower cut-off frequency giving less ripple and thus corresponding to a longer averaging time. The relationship between lowpass filter characteristic and effective averaging time will now be examined in some detail.

From Equation 3.3 the short-term average of a function $y(t)$ from $-T/2$ to $+T/2$ is given by $1/T \int_{-T/2}^{T/2} y(t) dt$, but more generally the running average obtained at time t over the previous T will be seen to be

$$\langle y \rangle_t = \frac{1}{T} \int_{t-T}^{t} y(\tau) \, d\tau \qquad (3.4)$$

as illustrated in Fig.3.12(a).

It will be found, however, that this can equally well be written as the (scaled) convolution equation

$$\langle y \rangle_t = \frac{1}{T} \int_{-\infty}^{\infty} y(\tau) g(t - \tau) \, d\tau \qquad (3.5)$$

where $g(\tau)$ is defined as follows:

$$
\begin{aligned}
g(\tau) &= 1 & 0 < \tau < T \\
g(\tau) &= 0 & \text{otherwise}
\end{aligned}
\qquad (3.6)
$$

To make this more obvious, Fig.3.12(b), (c), (d) and (e) illustrate $g(\tau)$, $g(-\tau)$, $g(t-\tau)$ and $y(\tau) g(t-\tau)$ respectively.

This convolution in the time domain corresponds to a multiplication in the frequency domain of the respective Fourier transforms. The amplitude spectrum of the rectangular function $g(t)$ defined in Eqn. (3.6) is once again the well-known $|sin\ x/x|$ function with zeroes at multiples

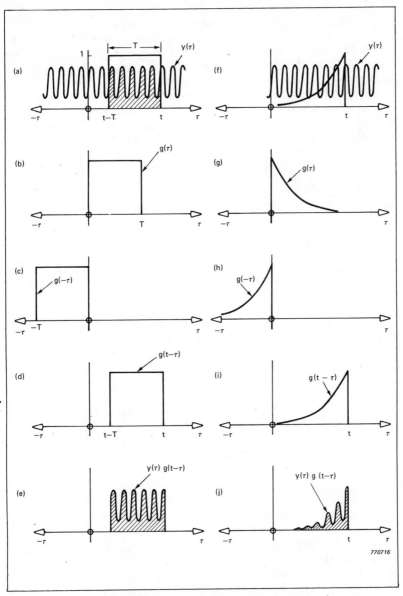

Fig.3.12. Running average as a convolution
(a)—(e) Linear weighting
(f)—(j) Exponential weighting

of *1/T* (Appendix A) and this is found to be a low-pass filter characteristic with a slope of —20 dB per decade from a cut-off frequency of *1/πT*. The positive half of this characteristic is illustrated on log-log scales in Fig.3.13. Note that the zeroes at multiples of *1/T* correspond to integral numbers of periods, and thus as pointed out in Section 2.2.1 integration over any integral number of periods completely removes the fluctuation. Note also that the phase characteristic of the Fourier transform of *g(τ)* has no influence on the power transmission, only on the phase shift of the ripple component.

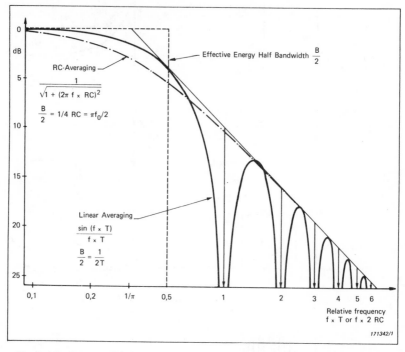

Fig.3.13. Comparison of linear and RC-averaging in frequency domain

Comparing Eqn.(3.5) with Eqn.(2.28) it will be seen that *g(τ)* as defined in Eqn.(3.6) can be interpreted as the required impulse response of a circuit to give running linear integration over averaging time *T*. This would be extremely difficult to realise in practice, and it is more common to use other electronic circuits with a low-pass filtering effect. The most commonly used circuit is a so-called RC circuit which has an impulse response defined by:

$$g(t) = 0 \qquad -\infty < t < 0$$
$$g(t) = e^{-t/RC} \qquad 0 < t < \infty$$

(3.7)

The employment of such a characteristic is referred to as "RC-averaging" or "exponential averaging" since the impulse response is a decaying exponential with most weight on the most recent part of the signal.

Fig.3.12(f) to (j) illustrate the resulting convolution for comparison with the rectangular function of Eqn.(3.6).

Fig.3.14 also compares a typical RC characteristic with a rectangular one. It has intentionally been scaled in such a way that $T = 2RC$, since with a peak response equal to twice that of the rectangular response the area under the two curves is the same, and thus the scaling will be the same for averaging of stationary signals. More importantly,

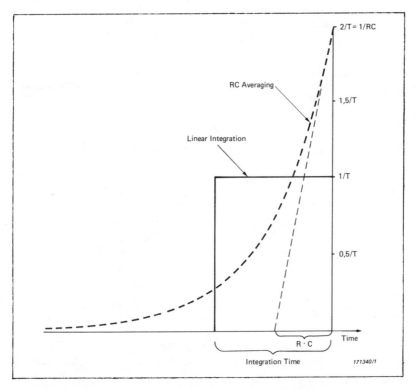

Fig.3.14. Weighting curves for linear and RC-integration

however, it is found that with $T = 2RC$, the two filter characteristics in the frequency domain have the same asymptotic lines and the same effective bandwidths. (See Fig.3.13.) The frequency response corresponding to the exponential characteristic of Equation (3.7) and drawn in Fig.3.13 is derived in Appendix A.

Thus, for an averaging time equal to several ripple periods (as will normally be required in practice to reduce ripple to an acceptable level) it will be seen that because the lowpass filter characteristics have the same asymptotic lines the maximum ripple which can be obtained with linear averaging over time T_A is the same as that obtained by exponential averaging with an RC-time constant such that

$$T_A = 2RC \qquad (3.8)$$

and thus Eqn. (3.8) expresses the equivalent averaging time for an RC circuit applied to a sinusoidal signal.

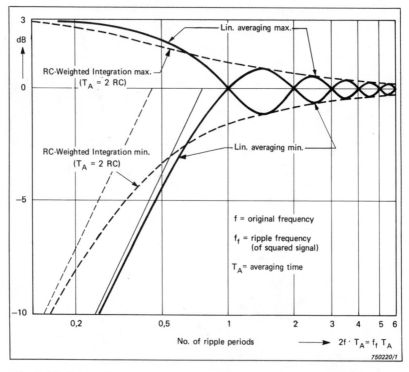

Fig.3.15. Comparison of ripple components for linear and RC averaging of squared sinewaves

66

The ripple obtained for averaging over various numbers of periods (Ref. 3.1) is illustrated in Fig.(3.15).

When the signal coming from the filter is narrow band random noise (i. e. the result of filtering wideband noise with a narrow band filter) it is found (Appendix B) that the relative fluctuation (variance) of the result is proportional to the noise bandwidth of the lowpass filter characteristic. It has already been shown that for the $|sin\ x/x|$ characteristic resulting from a rectangle of length T the noise bandwidth is $1/T$ (see Appendix A) and in Appendix A it is demonstrated that the noise bandwidth of the lowpass filter characteristic corresponding to exponential averaging is also the same for the situation illustrated in Fig.3.13 (i. e. with the same asymptotic lines) and thus Equation (3.8) also expresses the equivalent averaging time for stationary random signals. In Ref.3.1 it is shown that the same equivalence holds for trains of impulses (see

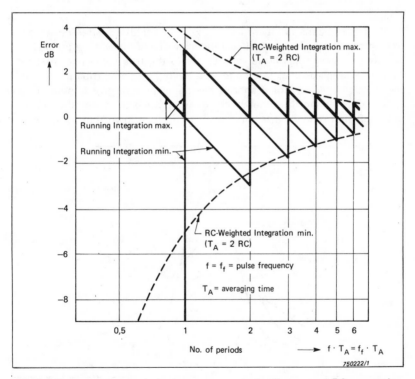

Fig.3.16. Comparison of ripple components for linear and RC averaging of pulse trains

Fig.3.16) so that it can be taken that Equation (3.8) holds for all stationary signals.

Figs.3.15 and 3.16 can be used for choosing averaging times for measurements on deterministic signals, according to the desired level of ripple. For random signals, the approach is somewhat different. In Appendix B it is shown that when a narrow band noise of bandwidth B is applied to an RMS detector with averaging time T_A the relative standard deviation of the measured RMS level is expressed by the equation:

$$\epsilon = \frac{1}{2\sqrt{BT_A}} \qquad \text{(for } BT_A \gg 1) \qquad (3.9)$$

or, in decibel form $\quad \epsilon = \dfrac{4{,}34}{\sqrt{BT_A}} \, dB$ $\qquad\qquad$ (3.9a)

What this means is illustrated in Fig.3.17 for three different averaging times. The result is itself a random variable but with a probability distribution which lies closer and closer to the true value (i. e. that for infinite averaging time) the longer the averaging time. Thus it is possible, though unlikely, for a shorter averaging time to give a more accurate result, but on the other hand, by integrating over the different regions of the probability density curve it can be shown that for a single

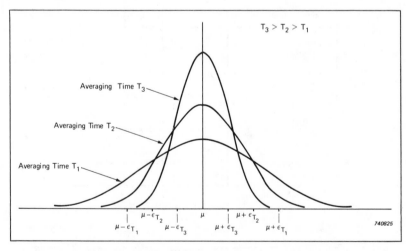

Fig.3.17. Influence of the averaging time on the error distribution

68

estimate there is a 68,3% chance of it being within $\pm \epsilon$ of the true value, 95,5% chance of it being within $\pm 2\epsilon$ and 99,7% of it being within $\pm 3\epsilon$.

Note that the equivalence expressed in Equation (3.8) does not apply to transient signals, but this point is discussed in some detail in the sections dealing with the analysis of transients.

3.2.3. Square Root Extraction

In Section 3.2.1 it was explained how a squaring circuit could be used to square an input signal $x(t)$ such that the output $y(t)$ could be represented by the equation

$$y(t) = kx^2(t) \qquad (3.10)$$

where k is a constant determining the size of the parabola. (Note that k is large for a narrow parabola and vice versa.)

In Section 3.2.2 it was shown that it was possible using an RC circuit to obtain the average of the squared signal. Thus:

$$\overline{y(t)} = k\ \overline{x^2(t)} \qquad (3.11)$$

In the foregoing it was assumed that the parameter k was a constant, but it is possible to feed back the circuit output signal in such a way that k is variable and proportional to the reciprocal of the output level. The output will thereby be modified, and will be called $y'(t)$. Thus, k can be expressed in the form:

$$k = \frac{k_1}{y'(t)} \qquad (3.12)$$

where k_1 is a constant
and $y'(t)$ is a slowly varying function of time because of
                the inherent averaging time.

Substituting this in an equation analogous to (3.11) gives

$$y'(t) = \frac{k_1}{y'(t)}\ \overline{x^2(t)}$$

$$\text{or} \quad \{y'(t)\}^2 = k_1\overline{x^2(t)}$$

$$\text{and} \quad y'(t) = \sqrt{k_1 \overline{x^2(t)}} \tag{3.13}$$

a scaled approximation to the RMS value of $x(t)$. It will be seen that a large RMS level gives a small k factor and thus a wide parabola as illustrated in Fig.3.10.

The square root extraction properties of the variable-parabola Wahrman detector are discussed in considerably more depth in Ref.3.1 where a more rigorous derivation of its mode of operation is given.

3.2.4. Logarithmic Conversion

The result will most frequently be required on a logarithmic, or decibel, amplitude scale and this may be achieved in a logarithmic conversion circuit at the analyzer output, or by using a logarithmic potentiometer in the Level Recorder used to record the spectrum.

3.2.5. Other Detector Types

In some newer instruments another type of detector known as an LMS (logarithmic mean square) detector is used. This makes use of the logarithmic characteristic of certain diodes to logarithmically convert the input signal. Squaring is achieved by amplifying the log converted signal by a factor of 2 and mean square averaging carried out in a part of the circuit where the signal has been exponentiated (antilogarithmically converted). The output voltage is proportional to the logarithm of the mean square value and can thus be scaled directly in dB. Details of its operation and characteristics are given in Ref.3.2. In comparison with the Wahrman detector already described, it can be said to have a true squaring characteristic, in general with a very high crest factor capability. The averaging is of the RC type so that the discussion of Section 3.2.2 still applies. The response of the detector to impulses is different, and is treated separately in Section 3.7 on the subject of impulse analysis.

In instruments such as digital filters and FFT analyzers, the calculation of mean square values is performed digitally and for example, the squaring operation is correct within the limitations of the number of bits used in the calculations. Provided the sampling theorem is obeyed, no errors arise from the sampling in time. One advantage of digital detection is that it normally permits a choice between linear integration (over a fixed time interval rather than a running average) and exponentially weighted averaging to which the results of Section 3.2.2 can be applied. Ref. 3.1 compares stepwise as well as running linear averaging with exponential averaging.

3.2.6. Detector Response

The effect of the finite detector response time on a swept frequency analysis is to give both a delay and an error on peaks (and valleys) in a spectrum compared with the true result which would be achieved with an infinitely slow rate of sweep (see Fig.3.18). Moreover, in particular with RC averaging, there is a limit to the steepness of slope which can be reproduced. These factors have been studied in some detail in Ref.3.1 and the results are expressed in Figs.3.19, 3.20 and 3.21. Fig.3.19 expresses the errors which will be experienced at peaks and valleys in a spectrum with running linear integration and RC-integration. Fig.3.20 gives information as to the corresponding delays. Finally, Fig.3.21 gives the delays which will be experienced at sloping areas in the spectrum. Here it is seen that for RC-integration there is an asymptotic limit of 8,7 dB/2RC which is the maximum rate at which the detector level can fall, and this will often govern the rate of sweep.

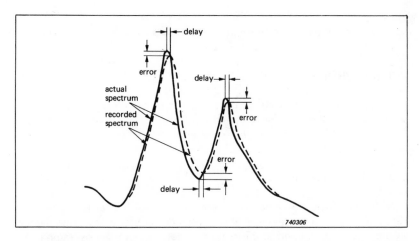

Fig.3.18. Error and delay (bias errors) in writing out peaks and valleys in a spectrum

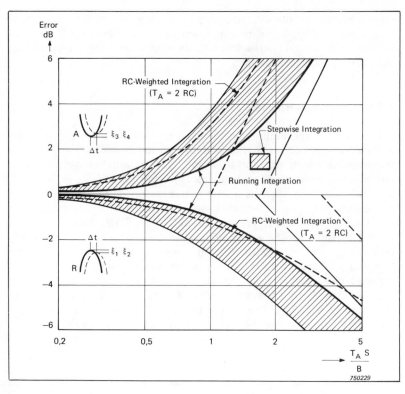

Fig.3.19. Errors at peaks and valleys in a recorded spectrum

3.3. RECORDERS

The level recorder used to record the spectrum can be the factor which most limits the sweep speed but its influence is greatly affected by whether it is operating in "AC-recording" or "DC-recording" mode.

3.3.1. AC Recording

AC-recording is the case where the filtered AC signal is applied directly to the recorder input. With the recorder set to "RMS", the signal is rectified and squared as for a normal detector but the averaging results entirely from the response of the pen drive system which acts as a lowpass filter.

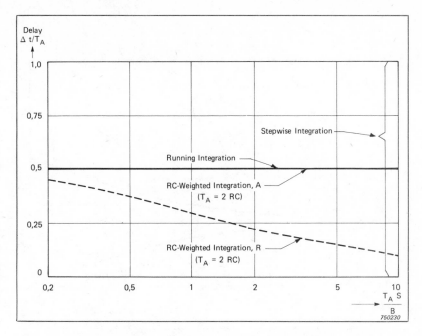

Fig.3.20. Delays at peaks and valleys in a recorded spectrum

Fig.3.22 shows typical frequency response characteristics (Ref.3.3) for the 2305 Level Recorder (for 50 mm paper), which illustrate the fact that higher writing speeds give a higher cut-off frequency and thus a shorter averaging time as would be expected from the discussion of Section 3.2.2. However, the level recorder circuits have a non-linear characteristic because of feedback of the error signal and also because of velocity limiting circuits which come more and more into play the larger the fluctuations. Accordingly, the lowpass filter characteristics illustrated in Fig.3.22 are not general but apply to a particular set of conditions, and in general there is a range of averaging times which apply to a given set writing speed. This range is illustrated in Fig.3.23 which shows the relationship between averaging time and writing speed for the B & K Level Recorders Types 2305, 2307 and 2306 (i. e. the results are not identical for all three, but all tend to fall in the range indicated by the shaded area). In general the lower values of averaging time apply for small fluctuations while the higher values apply to large fluctuations.

Thus, in order to obtain a given averaging time with AC-recording,

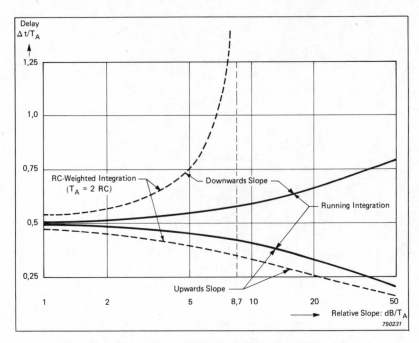

Fig.3.21. Delays at sloping areas in a recorded spectrum

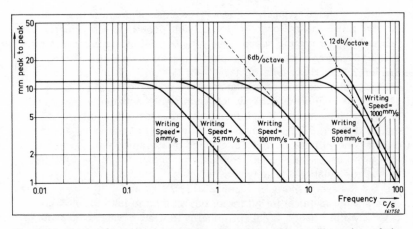

Fig.3.22. Typical frquency response curves for "normal" setting of the Recorder control knob marked "Potentiometer Range dB". The curves were measured for a fixed maximum amplitude and different writing speeds

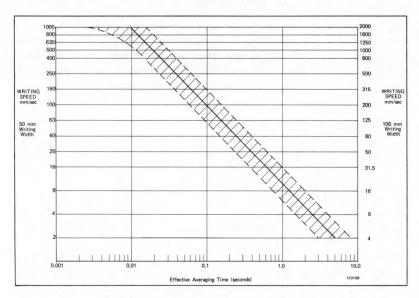

Fig.3.23. Averaging time vs writing speed

Fig.3.23 may be used to select an appropriate writing speed, and then the rate of sweep may be limited by the error introduced on peaks and valleys or, more likely, by being able to reproduce the steepest part of the spectrum with a limited writing speed.

3.3.2. DC Recording

In DC recording, the RC-averaged RMS level is applied to the input of the recorder which is then operated in "DC" mode. This requires of course that the analyzer being used has a DC output with a sufficiently large dynamic range (i. e. > 50 dB) but this being the case it is generally better to use DC recording for the following two reasons:

1) The averaging time is much better specified.

2) It is generally possible to analyze faster with DC recording.

Note that even in DC recording the pen system will still add an extra delay corresponding to its inherent averaging time. However, with both 2305 and 2307 Level Recorders it is always possible to select a Writing Speed of 1000 mm/s (100 mm paper). From Fig.3.23 its seen that

75

this corresponds to an averaging time of about 0,02 s and is thus negligibly small in comparison with the smallest averaging time available for DC recording (0,1 s). It is later shown (Section 3.5.2.7) that for this choice of writing speed the limitation on reproduction of slopes is also determined by the averaging time and not by the recorder.

3.4. ANALOG ANALYZER TYPES

Analog analyzers fall into the following broad categories:

(1) Discrete stepped filter analyzers
(2) Sweeping filter analyzers
(3) Parallel analyzers (real-time)
(4) Time compression analyzers (real-time)

Time compression analyzers have been included, even though they make use of digital techniques, because the actual frequency analysis is carried out by analog (heterodyne) techniques.

The mode of operation and other main features of each of these types will now be discussed in more detail.

3.4.1. Discrete Stepped Filter Analyzers

Fig.3.24 shows a simple block diagram of a typical fixed filter analyzer. The signal, after conditioning by an input amplifier, is applied in parallel to a bank of filters, contiguous in the frequency domain, which together cover the frequency range of interest (Fig.3.25). A detector is connected sequentially to the various filter outputs, and thus successively measures the output power in each frequency band. Note that it is not necessary to wait for the filter response time, only that of the detector.

The rate of stepping through the various filters is often controlled by and synchronized with the speed of a connected level recorder, which can thus be used to record the resulting spectrum. A typical 1/3-octave spectrum obtained in this way is shown in Fig.3.26.

This principle is normally only used for bandwidths down to 1/3-octave, since the multitude of separate filters which would be required for a narrow-band analysis would be prohibitive in cost.

76

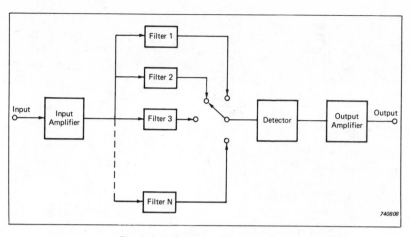

Fig.3.24. Stepped filter analyzer

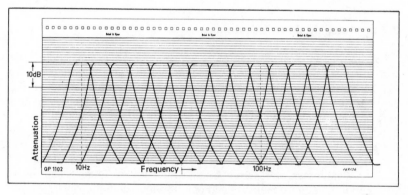

Fig.3.25. Frequency response of several adjacent 1/3-octave filters

A more up-to-date way of achieving the same effect as a filter bank is to have only two filters whose centre frequencies can be changed by switching between different electronic components. These two filters can be designed to step up alternately in frequency in such a way that the signal is always being applied to the next filter in the series while measurements are being made with the current filter. This gives effectively the same result as a complete bank of parallel filters in the sense that every filter has had adequate time to respond before the detector is coupled in to its output.

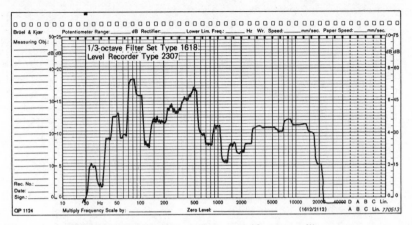

Fig.3.26. Typical spectrum from a 1/3-octave filter set

3.4.2. Sweeping Filter Analyzers

For narrow-band analysis it is more common to use a single filter with tunable centre frequency, as illustrated in block diagram form in Fig.3.27. The filter can be either of constant bandwidth or constant percentage bandwidth type. Fig.3.28 shows an analysis obtained in this way on the same signal as in Fig.3.26, in the first place with the same bandwidth (1/3-octave or 23,1%) and then with 1% bandwidth. The analysis range has been restricted to the decade 200 — 2000 Hz, and can be compared with this decade in Fig.3.26. Instead of a number of spectrum estimates at discrete frequencies, the resulting spectrum is now continuous in frequency. Each point on the curve, however, represents an integration of the true spectrum over a frequency range corresponding to the filter bandwidth. Considering only the positive frequency components in both signal spectrum and filter characteristic, it will be seen that the result is effectively a convolution of the two func-

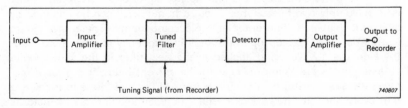

Fig.3.27. Sweeping filter analyzer

78

tions. (It may in fact be of assistance in the interpretation of convolution to think of it as a sweeping filtration of one function with the other reversed.)

3.4.3. Real-time Parallel Analyzers

The two types of analyzers already discussed are known as sequential or serial analyzers, since the analysis is carried out sequentially at each frequency. Thus, the assumption is implicitly made that the signal being analyzed is stationary, because otherwise the analysis at one frequency would have no connection with the analysis at another frequency (which is made on a different section of the time signal). Sometimes a signal is forced to be stationary by recording a section of it on a tape loop (or equivalent) which is played back repetitively.

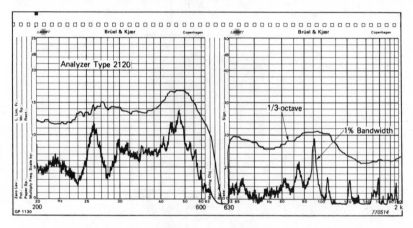

Fig.3.28. Sweeping filter analysis for comparison with Fig.3.26

So-called real-time analyzers obtain the whole spectrum in parallel from the same section of signal, and are thus not only able to follow changing signals, but can also obtain the spectrum very much faster than sequential analyzers. Perhaps the most direct way of performing such a real-time analysis is simply to apply the signal to a parallel bank of filter/amplifier/detector channels as illustrated in block diagram form in Fig.3.29. Such an analyzer is called a parallel analyzer and the first real-time 1/3-octave analyzers (e. g. B & K Type 3347) were made in this way. The speed with which the results are generated makes it desirable to be able to view them on a continuously updated screen, and

79

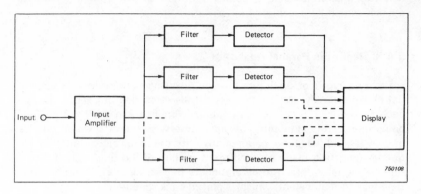

Fig.3.29. Real-time parallel analyzer

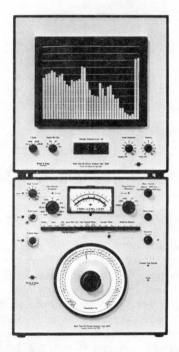

Fig.3.30. Real-time 1/3-octave Analyzer Type 3347

also to be able to transfer them rapidly in digital form to a computer or other digital device. Fig.3.30 shows the B & K Analyzer Type 3347.

The analog parallel analyzer has now been superseded by analyzers based on digital filtering (see Chapter 4) but its operation will be discussed wherever relevant, since many are still in service.

3.4.4. Time Compression Analyzers

The parallel channel approach could not be applied economically for bandwidths narrower than 1/3-octave (i. e. of the order of 30 channels over 3 decades), and for narrow band real-time analysis another approach is necessary. The first successful narrow band real-time analyzers were based on the so-called "time compression" principle, which can be briefly explained as follows:

The analysis time (per filter) is found to be always limited by expressions of the kind

$$BT_D \geqslant K \qquad (3.14)$$

where B is the filter bandwidth
        T_D is the time required per bandwidth (dwell time)
and K is a constant.

For example, with a deterministic signal, T_D is normally governed by the filter response time as given in Equation (3.1). For random signals T_D is governed by the averaging time which in turn is determined by equation (3.9). These equations are both of the form of Eqn.(3.14).

Thus, the only way of decreasing the analysis time per channel (T_D) is to increase the bandwidth B. This can in fact be done without affecting the resolution by recording a signal at one speed and then playing it back M times faster. As will be seen from Fig.3.31 all frequencies will then be multiplied by M, and thus the same resolution can be achieved with a filter bandwidth which is M times larger. Thus, T_D can be reduced by a factor of M which is the same as saying that the analysis can be carried out M times faster.

Use can be made of this fact in a simple way when it is possible to record on an FM tape recorder at a low speed and play back at the highest tape speed. This applies to recordings on a reel or a loop. On the other hand the speedup ratios which can be achieved by this means are quite limited (generally of the order of 10).

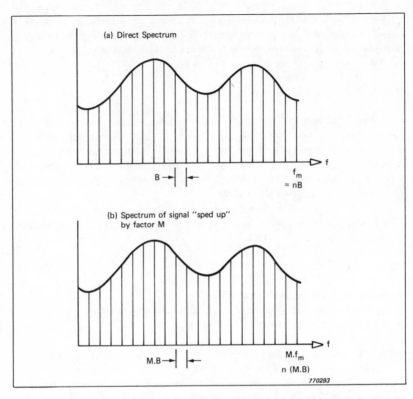

Fig.3.31. Effect on spectrum of playing back a signal M times faster

This limitation is removed by employing a digital memory as the intermediate recording medium since a speedup ratio of several thousand can then be achieved quite easily. It will be appreciated that if the speedup ratio M is greater than the number of analysis channels, then the entire analysis can be obtained in the time required to collect the data for the analysis of one channel only. Even so, if the analysis system is such that it is necessary to first record a signal sample and then play it back for analysis, then it cannot be considered "real-time" because the continuation of the signal is ignored during the analysis. This principle may be termed "high speed analysis" and is discussed in detail in Section 3.5.3.

Real-time analyzers based on the time compression principle utilise the technique of recording in a digital memory and playing back at high speed, but are so designed that it is possible to continually update the

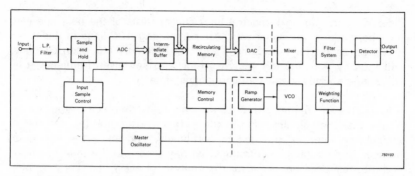

Fig.3.32. Block diagram of analyzer section of Time Compression Analyzer Type 3348

recorded signal while the analysis is going on. The block diagram of the analyzer section of a typical instrument (B & K Type 3348) is shown in Fig.3.32 and its operation in the highest real-time frequency range (10 kHz) will be described.

The incoming signal is lowpass filtered at the highest frequency of interest (i. e. 10 kHz). This is to permit a sample rate in the Analog/Digital converter of 3 times this or 30 kHz. The cutoff rate of the filter must be quite steep to avoid "aliasing" (see Section 2.2.4) in the working range.

Thus three samples represent one period of the highest frequency, and the 1200 word memory will contain 400 periods of this frequency. The lowest frequency which can be analyzed corresponds to one period in the memory and thus the ratio from the lowest to the highest is 400. This is the same as saying that it is possible to perform a 400 line analysis on a linear frequency scale where the bandwidth is equal to the line spacing.

For the analysis of each line in the spectrum, the memory is played back 400 times faster than recorded (i. e. 12 MHz sample rate corresponding to 100 μs for the memory length). The maximum frequency is thus transformed up to 4 MHz and this corresponds to 400 lines each with 10 kHz bandwidth and separation. A 10 kHz bandwidth heterodyne filter followed by a detector can thus be used to obtain the spectral component in one of these bands. At the end of the 100 μs, another 3 samples have arrived from the A/D converter and are stored in an intermediate buffer (Fig.3.32). These are now introduced into the main memory to replace the 3 oldest samples, and the filter centre frequency is indexed up to the next spectral line. The analysis of the next line can then be made in the same way. After analyzing 400 lines in this way, it will be seen that the whole 1200 word memory has been changed and thus by the time the analyzer returns to any given frequency it is operating on entirely new (but contiguous) data.

In any lower frequency range, the only real difference in the operation is that the sampling rate of the A/D converter (and the associated antialiasing filter) is changed proportionally, and since the minimum number of data samples introduced at any time into the main memory is three, this does not occur for the analysis of every line. For example, for 5 kHz frequency range it occurs every second line; for 2 kHz frequency range every fifth line, and so on. The analyzer still produces spectra at the same rate, but each one is no longer independent, since the memory is only completely changed every second spectrum at 5 kHz, every fifth at 2 kHz and so on.

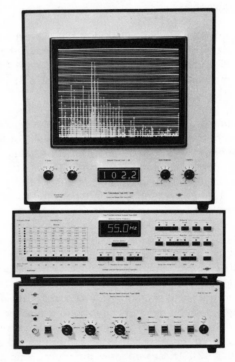

Fig.3.33. Time Compression Analyzer Type 3348

An averager is an integral part of the instrument and permits averaging over a selected number of independent spectra, in order to improve the stability of the result. The averaging can be carried out with either a linear or exponential weighting, the latter giving a continuously updated result. Selection of averaging time is discussed in detail in Section 3.5.4.

The appearance of the analyzer Type 3348 is as shown in Fig.3.33.

3.5. PRACTICAL ANALYSIS OF STATIONARY SIGNALS

The analysis of stationary signals, both deterministic and random, will now be discussed with respect to choice of analysis parameters for each of the types of analyzer discussed in Section 3.4.

3.5.1. Stepped Filter Analysis (1/3 octave and octave)

In this case, the analysis bandwidth is determined by the analyzer, and the only choice to be made is between 1/3 octave and octave. The discussion here will refer to 1/3 octave unless otherwise specified.

The parameters to be chosen are the following:

1. Averaging time, T_A
2. DC or AC recording
3. Recorder writing speed
4. Recorder paper speed

Unless otherwise specified, it will be assumed that B & K standard calibrated paper of width 100 mm is used, on which 1/3 octave corresponds to 5 mm in the longitudinal direction, and that the recorder is a B & K Level Recorder Type 2307 or 2305.

3.5.1.1. Averaging Time T_A

For **deterministic** signals, the major requirement is that ripple be reduced to an acceptable level. Where only a single sinusoidal component is included in the bandwidth, Fig.3.15 indicates that the ripple will be reduced to less than ± 1/4 dB for

85

$$T_A \geqslant \frac{3}{f} \qquad\qquad (3.15)$$

where f is the frequency of the single component. Where there are several sinusoidal components within the bandwidth (and this is quite likely with 1/3-octave analysis) then Eqn. 3.15 can still be used, with f interpreted as the minimum separation of any two components, since this will represent the lowest beat frequency●. When there are a large number of sinusoidal components in the bandwidth such as is likely at high frequencies, then strictly speaking the same considerations still apply but the situation becomes similar to the case of random signals and it might be simplest to treat the signal as random.

For **random** signals, Eqn.(3.9) can be used to select a suitable value for T_A, depending on the desired accuracy. Table 3.1 summarizes the values of standard deviation (in dB) obtained over a range of averaging times and frequencies. It will normally be the lowest frequency of interest which governs the selection of averaging time, but it will be noted that for every half decade increase in frequency it is possible to reduce the averaging time by a factor of $\sqrt{10}$, the normal steps in B & K measuring amplifiers. The newer filter sets can control the changes in averaging time automatically.

Std error for T_A	Centre Frequency (Hz)								
	2	6,3	20	63	200	630	2k	6,3k	20k
0,1 s						1,2	0,7	0,4	0,2
0,3					1,2	0,7	0,4	0,2	
1				1,2	0,7	0,4	0,2		
3			1,2	0,7	0,4	0,2			
10		1,2	0,7	0,4	0,2				
30	1,2	0,7	0,4	0,2					
100	0,7	0,4	0,2						
300	0,4	0,2							

Table 3.1. Standard error (dB) for 1/3-octave filters in combination with various averaging times

For **octave-band** filters, the bandwidth is of course 3 times larger, so that averaging times from Table 3.1 should be reduced by a factor of 3 (one step).

● The beat frequency will not be doubled by squaring (as for a single component) and therefore it may be found necessary on inspection to increase T_A even further

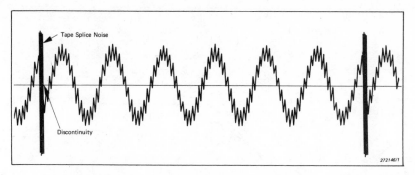

Fig.3.34. Disturbances associated with a tape loop

For **signals recorded on a loop** i. e. tape loop or Digital Event Recorder, it can be advantageous to make the averaging time a number of times longer than the loop circulation time, regardless of whether the original signal is random or deterministic. This is done for the practical reason of eliminating fluctuations due to the discontinuity at the loop junction. The influence of the junction is two-fold (see Fig.3.34).

1. The discontinuity in the signal itself has been introduced artificially, but its effect is calculable and discussed in detail in Section 3.5.3. This is the only effect in the case of a Digital Event Recorder.

2. In the case of a tape loop, the tape joint itself can introduce extraneous noise. This is usually worst for FM (frequency modulation) recording, since not only the signal, but also the carrier frequency is discontinuous at the junction.

The signal can be considered as stationary, with a set of superimposed impulses spaced at intervals corresponding to the loop length. Fig.3.16 indicates that to reduce the ripple of such a pulse train even to ± 0,75 dB would require an averaging time about 6 times the pulse spacing, but in practice it is found that a factor of 3 is often adequate, partly because the pulses are lengthened by passage through the filter, and partly because their effect (as shown in Section 3.5.3) is only apparent in the filter flanks and not at peaks in the spectrum.

Where the signal recorded on the loop is random, it should be kept in mind that the effective integration time (for insertion in Eqn. 3.9) is now limited by the loop length, and from that point of view it is inefficient to use a longer averaging time. In this respect there is a difference between linear and RC averaging. In Ref. 2.2 the effective integra-

87

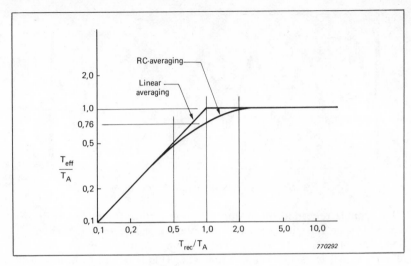

Fig.3.35. Effect of record length (T_{rec}) and averaging time (T_A) on effective integration time (T_{eff})

tion time is studied as a function of loop length and averaging time, and the results are reproduced here in Fig.3.35. From this it is seen that for an exponential averaging time equal to the loop length the effective integration time is reduced to 76% (of either), but a factor of at least 2 either way ensures that the integration time is equal to the shorter of the two. Thus, no further statistical benefit can be obtained from making the averaging time more than twice the loop length (for RC averaging), or one times the loop length (for linear averaging).

Note that with AC recording, the effective averaging time with respect to pulses is much greater than indicated in Fig.3.23 and thus in general the selection of averaging time can be based solely on the stationary part of the signal.

3.5.1.2. DC or AC Recording

As mentioned in Section 3.3.2 it is generally better to use DC recording where this is possible, but where no DC output is available from the analyzer (or where it has a dynamic range less than 50 dB) it is necessary to use AC recording.

Where one has a choice, it may be worth checking both possibilities with respect to paper speed as in some cases AC recording is just as fast, and may be preferable for another reason (e. g. to obtain averaging times less than 0,1 s).

3.5.1.3. Writing Speed

For **DC recording** it is always possible to select a writing speed of 1000 mm/s (100 mm paper) and this is always advisable with the Level Recorder Type 2307. With the Level Recorder Type 2305 it may be preferred to use a lower writing speed (to reduce hum which results from the low chopper frequency). The effect of using 315 mm/s will be very small, even with the lowest averaging time of 0,1 s.

For **AC recording**, the writing speed will be determined by the required averaging time, and can be selected using Fig.3.23.

3.5.1.4. Paper Speed

The selection of a suitable paper speed will be described for the case where it is the level recorder which controls the rate of stepping between filters. Newer filter sets control the rate of stepping in proportion to the averaging time which is changed automatically, but because the operation in that case is virtually automatic, it does not require operator intervention.

In the first-mentioned case, the paper speed should be chosen such that the pen can attain the correct level for each 1/3-octave band and remain at that level for a while before shifting to the next filter (see Fig.3.36).

For **DC recording**, it will normally be the rate of fall of the detector which limits the sweep rate, and from Fig.3.21 of Section 3.2.6 it will be remembered that this has a maximum of 8,7 dB/averaging time.

Table 3.2 gives suitable paper speeds for the normal range of averaging times, based on the assumption that the time required to sweep over a bandwidth is equal to 5 averaging times. With B & K's steepest filter characteristics this means that the step between filters will normally be attained in less than 2 mm (i. e. 40% of the bandwidth), and in the very worst case of a single sinusoidal component located between two filters, within 75% of the bandwidth. This worst case situation is illustrated in Fig.3.37.

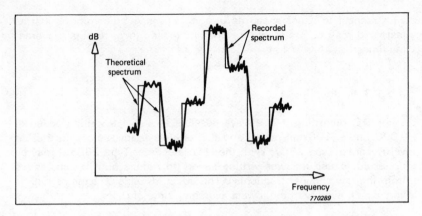

Fig.3.36. Typical recorded spectrum

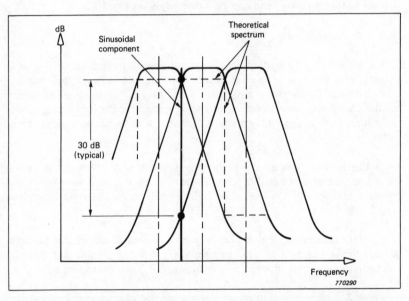

Fig.3.37. "Worst-case" situation involving largest possible step between adjacent filters

In cases where the spectrum is known to be relatively flat, with a maximum fall of approx. 5 dB between adjacent filters, it will be possible to increase paper speed by one step (i. e. a factor of approx. 3). The time taken to sweep over one bandwidth will then be approx. 1,6 times

90

Averaging Time T_A (s)	0,1	0,3	1	3	10	30	100	300
Paper speed for DC recording (mm/s)	10	3	1	0,3	0,1	0,03	0,01	0,003

Table 3.2. Paper Speeds for DC recording

the averaging time, and this is about the minimum time required for the detector to respond, even on peaks.

For **AC recording**, the same basic considerations apply, except that now it is the writing speed rather than the averaging time which will determine how rapidly the recording pen can adjust to a new level. Table 3.3 gives suitable paper speeds for the range of writing speeds available. Once again these may be increased by one step when the spectrum is known to be relatively flat.

Writing Speed (mm/s) (100 mm paper)	4	8—16	31,5—50	80—125	200—2000
Paper Speed for AC recording (mm/s)	0,1	0,3	1	3	10

Table 3.3. Paper Speeds for AC recording

For **octave-band** analysis, with either DC or AC recording, it is generally best to use the same values as for 1/3 octave, because the filters are occasionally formed by combining 3 adjacent 1/3-octave filters, and thus the slope of the filter characteristic is the same.

There is a chance, however, that the values recommended here can be increased by one step (in particular for octave analysis) and it is one of the features of stepped frequency analysis that this point can be checked by visual observation of the spectrum. This is not the case in general with swept frequency analysis.

3.5.2. Swept Filter Analysis

In this case there are several more factors to take account of, and in the most general case it will be necessary to consider the following:

(1) Constant vs. constant percentage bandwidth
(2) Linear vs. logarithmic frequency scale
(3) The actual bandwidth, in Hz or percentage
(4) Averaging time
(5) Dwell time per bandwidth (which determines the sweep rate)
(6) Recorder writing speed
(7) Recorder paper speed

These will each be discussed in turn.

3.5.2.1. Constant vs. Constant Percentage Bandwidth

From the discussion in Section 3.1 it will be appreciated that constant bandwidth is most appropriate in the following situations:

1. Where the frequency scale is linear.

2. Where the spectrum is dominated by harmonics or other discrete components (i. e. deterministic).

3. Where comparisons are to be made with inherently constant bandwidth analyses (e. g. FFT or time compression).

and that constant percentage bandwidth is most appropriate in the following situations:

1. Where the frequency scale is logarithmic.

2. Where the signal is stationary random and the spectrum dominated by resonant peaks. Note that bandwidth compensation will be required if the result is to be calibrated as a spectral density. See Section 3.5.2.9. This compensation may be included in the analyzer as a power attenuation factor proportional to the bandwidth.

3. In order to account simply for fluctuations in machine speed, either within one record or between several records.

4. Where constant percentage bandwidth is specified, as is often the case with, for example, acoustic measurements or whole body vibration.

5. Where comparisons are to be made with inherently constant percen-

tage bandwidth analyses (e. g. 1/3-octave).

In some cases it is possible to approximate constant percentage band-width by a series of constant bandwidth filters which step up automatically, for example, by a factor of $\sqrt{10}$ for every half decade in frequency. Note that in a broadband spectrum this would result in a sudden increase in spectrum level of 5 dB for every filter change, but that the step can be eliminated by using bandwidth compensation. At the same time this would automatically give a result in terms of spectral density. It is necessary, however. that the analyzer bandwidth is always less than that of any peaks in the signal spectrum, in order for the result to be valid.

3.5.2.2. Linear vs. Logarithmic Frequency Scale

From the discussion in Section 3.1 it will be appreciated that a linear frequency scale is most appropriate in the following situations:

1. Where the spectrum is dominated by harmonically related or other equi-spaced discrete components such as sidebands (and where constant bandwidth is used).

2. Where the frequency range is restricted.

3. Where comparisons are to be made with analyses which inherently have a linear frequency scale (e. g. FFT, time compression).

while a logarithmic frequency scale is most appropriate in the following situations:

1. Where constant percentage bandwidth filters are used.

2. Where a wide frequency range is to be covered.

3. In order to eliminate the effects of minor machine speed fluctuations by a lateral shift of the spectrum.

4. In order to emphasize relationships which are linear in log-log representations, e. g. integration (—20 dB/decade) and bandwidth compensation (—10 dB/decade).

Note that some analyzers (e. g. B & K Types 2120, 2121) employ a hyperbolic frequency scale which repeats for each half decade (e. g. Fig.3.28).

3.5.2.3. Choice of Bandwidth

It is found that the time required for a swept frequency analysis is proportional to the square of the reciprocal of the bandwidth, so it is important that the latter be chosen as large as possible while still giving adequate resolution.

For **deterministic** signals, as discussed in Section 2.4.1, it is desirable that the most closely spaced spectral components can be separated, and this will generally be the case if the bandwidth is made of the order of 1/3 of the minimum spacing (assuming a shape factor of about 5). See Fig.3.38.

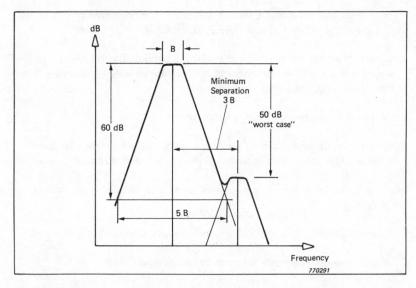

Fig.3.38. Minimum separation of sinusoidal components for filter shape factor 5 (typical)

For **random** signals, as discussed in Section 2.4.2, it is desirable for the percentage bandwidth to be chosen less than 1/3 of the width of the narrowest peak in the spectrum. In some cases it will only be possible to satisfy this requirement by using stepping constant bandwidth filters, since 1% bandwidth is typically the minimum constant percentage

94

bandwidth available. As previously mentioned, bandwidth compensation can be used to obtain a smooth result.

For **mixtures** of deterministic and random components it is generally best to base the selection of bandwidth on the deterministic components. In this case, if stepping bandwidth is used to cover a wide frequency range, it is best not to use bandwidth compensation, but to recognize and accept the sudden changes in level of the random components where the filter bandwidth changes.

3.5.2.4. Averaging Time T_A

Here, the discussion of Section 3.5.1.1 still applies, with the following additional remarks:

For **deterministic** signals, the minimum requirement is set by Equation (3.15) $(T_A \geqslant 3/f)$ and solutions of this can be obtained from Fig.3.41, but often this will be small in relationship to the filter response time which determines the analysis speed. Where DC recording is used, it is wise to increase the averaging time up to the maximum which does not affect the sweep speed. This limit is given in terms of T_D, the "dwell time per bandwidth" (see Section 3.5.2.5), by the equation:

$$T_A \leqslant \frac{T_D}{4} \qquad (3.16)$$

where allowance has been made for a filter characteristic with shape factor $> 4,5$.

For **random** signals, the selection of T_A should be based on Equation (3.9) $(\epsilon = 1/(2\sqrt{BT_A}))$ and Table 3.4 lists values of standard error ϵ against BT_A product. Moreover, Fig.3.41 permits the selection of T_A for various bandwidths and centre frequencies for a BT_A product of 10. This value of T_A can be modified proportionally for other BT_A products.

BT_A	10	20	30	40	50	80 ·	120
ϵ (dB)	1,5	1,0	0,8 ·	0,7	0,6	0,5	0,4

Table 3.4. Standard error ϵ vs. BT_A product

3.5.2.5. Filter Dwell Time T_D

The "filter dwell time" T_D is defined by the equation

$$S = \frac{B}{T_D} \tag{3.17}$$

where S is the sweep speed and B is the filter bandwidth

Note that S will be in Hz/s for B expressed in Hz, but will be in mm/s (paper speed) for B expressed in mm (equivalent length on the recording paper).

Thus T_D is the time taken to sweep over one bandwidth.

As mentioned previously, the sweep rate (and thus T_D) is limited by one or more of the factors:

1. Filter response time T_R
2. Averaging time T_A
3. Recorder writing speed W

and each of these will be considered in turn.

With respect to **filter response time** T_R, it will be appreciated that if T_D is made equal to T_R, then the recording of the whole spectrum will be delayed by an amount equal to the bandwidth (see Fig.3.39(a)). This is normally not acceptable, and it is customary to make

$$T_D = K_R T_R \tag{3.18}$$

where for example, $K_R = 4$ will give a delay equal to $1/4$ bandwidth (see Fig.3.39(b)). This is a good compromise as it corresponds to the average frequency error in the fixed filter case. Solutions are given for this case in the graph of Fig.3.41. Combining Equation (3.18) with Equation (3.1) of Section 3.1.2, one obtains the result:

$$BT_D = K_R \tag{3.19}$$

where K_R is to be chosen keeping in mind that the delay is equal to B/K_R. Equation (3.18) will normally govern for deterministic signals.

With respect to **averaging time** T_A, there are two basic considerations to be taken into account when selecting T_D. Letting:

$$T_D = K_A T_A \tag{3.20}$$

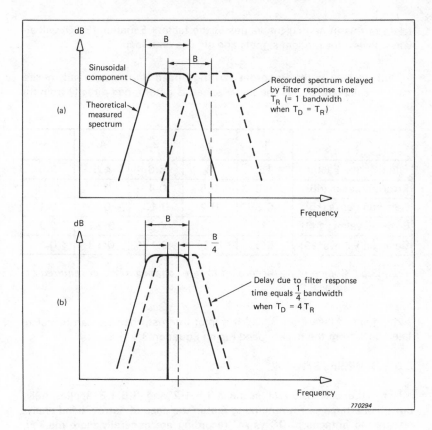

Fig.3.39. Effect of filter response time on recorded spectrum

Then K_A will either be limited by the maximum rate of fall of the detector ($8,7\,dB/T_A$, see Fig.3.21) which limits the ability to reproduce the filter characteristic, or by the maximum allowable errors and delays in recording peaks and valleys in the spectrum (Figs.3.19, 3.20). Table 3.5 allows selection of K_A based on these factors. With respect to the ability to reproduce the filter characteristic, this will primarily apply where the spectrum contains sinusoidal components. The filter shape factor to be used is not necessarily the actual value, but that corresponding to the steepest part of the characteristic. The error and delay on peaks and valleys (usually the former) will generally govern in the case of random signals where the analyzer bandwidth is normally less than that of the function being analyzed, and account has been taken of this in setting the values in the table.● Equation (3.20) will always govern for random signals and signals on a loop.

With respect to the **Recorder Writing Speed** W, it is not really necessary to calculate T_D , as the paper speed is determined directly from the

K_A	1	2	3	4	5
Filter Shape Factor	15	8	5,6	4,5	3,8
Error on peaks (dB)	1,2	0,5	0,4	0,2	0,15
Delay on peaks (×B)	0,3	0,2	0,13	0,1	0,1
Error on valleys (dB)	3	1	0,5	0,25	0,2
Delay on valleys (×B)	0,5	0,25	0,17	0,13	0,1

Table 3.5. Choice of K_A according to filter characteristic or required accuracy

writing speed (see Eqn. 3.22). If it is of interest, then T_D can be calculated back from the paper speed (using Equation 3.21).

3.5.2.6. Writing Speed W

Here, the discussion of sections 3.5.1.2 and 3.5.1.3 applies fully, but it is perhaps worth remarking that in the case of narrow band analysis, the advantages of DC vs AC recording are generally more marked, partly because the analysis time becomes more critical, and partly because the validity of the results is not so obvious by inspection, and thus the selection of parameters such as averaging time is made somewhat more conservatively.

3.5.2.7. Paper Speed P

As for the discussion of section 3.5.1.4, the selection of paper speed

---

● Errors and delays given in the table will be correct when the filter bandwidth is equal to that of peaks in the spectrum being analyzed. They may be underestimated when the signal bandwidth is less (e. g. discrete components), but then the filter shape factor would normally govern. When the filter bandwidth is less than that of peaks in the spectrum, the indicated errors will be conservative, and delays approximately correct

depends primarily on whether DC or AC recording is used.

For **DC recording**, the maximum paper speed may be obtained from Equation (3.17), expressed in the form

$$P = \frac{B_{eq}}{T_D} \qquad (3.21)$$

where B_{eq} is the equivalent of the bandwidth in mm along the recording paper.

There are two advantages in using this approach:

1. It is not necessary to go through the intermediate step of calculating the sweep rate in Hz/s.

2. Equation (3.21) is equally applicable to the case of constant bandwidth, where the bandwidth in Hz corresponds to a certain length in mm (on a linear scale), and to constant percentage bandwidth, where a given percentage corresponds to a certain length in mm (e. g. on a logarithmic scale).

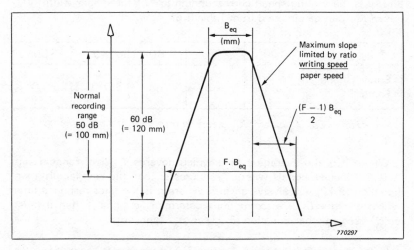

Fig.3.40. Limitation of writing speed in recording a filter characteristic of shape factor F

For **AC-recording**, the sweep rate will often be limited by the ability to write out the steepest filter flank with a given writing speed. Referring to Fig.3.40 it will be seen that the ratio of writing speed to paper speed must be greater than the slope of the filter characteristic which can be expressed as

$$\left(\frac{F-1}{2}\right)\frac{B_{eq}}{120}$$

where, as illustrated, F is the shape factor corresponding to the steepest part of the filter characteristic, and 120 mm is the paper width corresponding to 60 dB (i. e. assuming that 100 mm corresponds to 50 dB).

Thus, $$P \leqslant \frac{B_{eq}W}{K_W}$$ (3.22)

where $$K_W = \frac{240}{(F-1)}$$ (3.23)

and W is the writing speed corresponding to 100 mm paper width. Values of K_W can be obtained from Table 3.6.

K_W	100	75	50	40	30
Equiv. Shape Factor F	3,4	4,2	5,8	7,0	9,0

Table 3.6. Choice of K_W according to filter shape factor

Where it is the averaging time which governs T_D (i. e. random signals and looped signals where T_A is greater than the loop length) then Equation (3.22) will always govern. Where it is the filter response time which governs T_D (i. e. continuous deterministic signals) then it must be checked whether Equation (3.21) or (3.22) governs.

It has already been shown (section 3.3.2) that for DC recording, if a writing speed of 1000 mm/s is selected, then there is no effective increase in averaging time. It can be shown that there will be no limitation with respect to reproduction of filter slope either. The minimum averaging time available for DC recording with B & K analyzers is 0,1 s. Inserting this in Eqn. (3.20) with K_A = 2 (corresponding to Shape Factor 8) gives T_D = 0,2 s. Inserting this in turn in Equation (3.21) gives

$$P \leqslant \frac{B_{eq}}{0,2} = 5B_{eq}$$

Inserting the same shape factor in Equation (3.23) gives K_W = 34,3 and thus from Equation (3.22)

$$P \leqslant \frac{B_{eq} \cdot 1000}{34,3} = 29,2 \, B_{eq}$$

Accordingly, the limiting speed is almost 6 times faster, and thus Equation (3.21) will always govern.

3.5.2.8. Summary

It is probably necessary at this stage to summarize the most important information in the foregoing. Fig.3.41 indicates a logical procedure to be followed in the general case, and allows the most important parameters to be selected graphically. The following values have been chosen as most generally appropriate:

(1) K_R = 4 (See Section 3.5.2.5) i. e. $BT_D \geqslant 4$

(2) K_A = 2 (See Section 3.5.2.5) i. e. $T_D \geqslant 2 \, T_A$

(3) K_W = 50 (See Section 3.5.2.7) i. e. $P \leqslant B_{eq} \cdot W/50$

Note that the reason for the somewhat more conservative approach in selecting K_W compared with K_A (with respect to filter shape factor) is that the writing speed gives the same limitation for rising and falling curves, while the averaging time primarily limits falling curves only (and thus peaks are more likely to be recorded correctly).

3.5.2.9. Calibration

In the analysis of **deterministic** signals it is usual to express the results directly as an amplitude spectrum, where the amplitudes have the same dimensions as the input signal, e. g. volts. If the amplitudes are represented on a logarithmic scale then a ratio of 10 in amplitude corre-

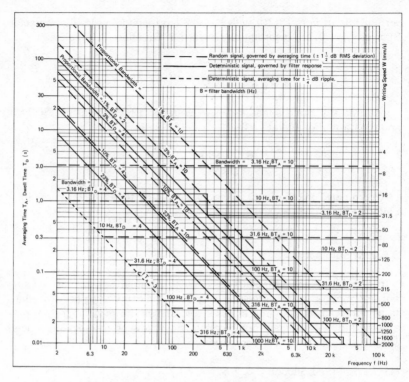

Fig.3.41. SWEEP SPEED FOR SWEPT FREQUENCY ANALYSIS
For each bandwidth and frequency range, determine Filter
Dwell Time, Averaging Time and Sweep Speed as follows:

1. Random Signal: *Dwell time T_D is always determined by averaging time T_A.*
From the graph read off T_A from the appropriate line for BT_A
= 10 (horizontal lines for constant bandwidth, sloping lines
for constant proportional bandwidth). This value will corre-
spond to ±1,5 dB RMS error. For a higher BT_A product and
consequent reduced error, increase the value of T_A propor-
tionally. Calculate $T_D = 2 T_A$.
For DC recording, calculate sweep speed $S = B/T_D$.
For AC recording, T_A is determined by recorder writing speed
W and this can be read directly from the right-hand scale.
Sweep speed can then be calculated from $S = BW/50$ (appli-
cable to 50 dB potentiometer and 100 mm paper).
2. Deterministic Signal *(periodic or quasi-periodic): Read T_D*

based on filter response time from appropriate line for BT_D = 4 (or 2 where bandwidth ≤ 1%). Read also minimum averaging time T_A based on ± 1/4 dB ripple from line fT_A = 3 (independent of bandwidth).

For DC recording, *calculate sweep speed based on filter response as $S = B/T_D$.*

For AC recording, *read off writing speed W corresponding to T_A and calculate sweep speed based on recorder response as $S = BW/50$. The governing sweep speed is the lesser of this and the value as calculated for DC recording.*

In all cases where sweep speed is governed by filter response time, increase T_A to the highest value which does not affect sweep speed. (i. e. $T_D/4$ for DC recording.)

Note (1) Averaging times will normally be constant over at least a half decade, whereas filter response times change automatically with frequency.

Note (2) S will be in Hz/s for B in Hz, but will be directly in mm/s for B expressed as equivalent recorder paper length in mm

sponds to 20 dB and Fig.3.42 can be used to convert to linear amplitudes within each 20 dB range. It is normal to set the full-scale value on the recording paper to a round figure (i. e. in 10 dB steps) and this can be done as follows:

1. Using the internal reference signal of the analyzer

This is typically 50 mV for B & K analyzers. With the analyzer in linear frequency mode (i. e. filter disconnected) and meter range 100 mV, the Level Recorder input attenuation is adjusted until the pen is 6 dB below full-scale. The full-scale on the paper then corresponds to the full-scale voltage of the meter for all the succeeding measure-

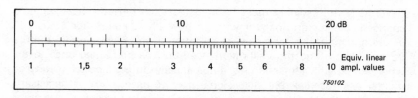

Fig.3.42. Linear amplitude vs. dB levels

103

ments. This full-scale voltage can easily be changed in 10 dB steps as required. Conversion of the scaling to mechanical units is straightforward provided the conversion factor of the input signal is known, (e. g. 10 mm/s per volt).

2. Using an external reference signal

This might for example be a pistonphone signal or the signal obtained from an accelerometer mounted on an accelerometer calibrator. The signal may either be played directly into the analyzer input or recorded on a tape recorder. To illustrate the general method, the case will be taken of an accelerometer calibrator which gives a vibration level of 1 g peak (i. e. 0,7 g RMS). The signal from the measurement system is played into the input of the analyzer (which is in linear mode) and the recorder pen adjusted to 3 dB below full-scale. The full-scale will now correspond to 1 g RMS and all later measurements can be related to this, taking due account of any 10 dB steps in amplification of either the measurement, analysis, or recording systems.

In the case of **random** signals, the results may be expressed as an amplitude spectrum, but it may be preferred to express them as a power spectral density (PSD).

For **constant bandwidth** analysis this only involves a modification of the scaling as follows:

The PSD is obtained by squaring the linear amplitude and dividing by the filter bandwidth, and the result is of course independent of frequency,

e. g.   for a full-scale level of 10 g and 100 Hz bandwidth
the full-scale power = $100 \, g^2$
and full-scale PSD = $100 \, g^2 / 100 \, Hz = 1 \, g^2 / Hz$

Normally, this scaling must be adjusted each time the bandwidth is changed, but for an analyzer with "bandwidth compensation" it is adjusted automatically, by means of an attenuation proportional to the filter bandwidth, and the calibration need only be performed once, even where the bandwidth changes automatically during normal measurements. A sinusoidal reference signal may be used, but it is necessary to make the calibration adjustments with the filter selected, and thus the filter must be centred on the reference signal so as not to attenuate it.

104

For **constant percentage bandwidth** analysis of **random** signals the bandwidth varies proportionally with the frequency, and thus the conversion factor to calibrate as a PSD varies with frequency. On the normal log-log paper used for 1/3-octave analysis the conversion factor is linear and corresponds to a linear slope of -3 dB/octave (-10 dB/decade). Thus, if the conversion to PSD is performed at one frequency (e. g. 100 Hz) then it is relatively simple to draw lines of constant PSD through the values calculated at 100 Hz and sloping upwards at 10 dB/decade with increasing frequency. Fig.3.43 illustrates a typical example. Alternatively, an instrument is available which gives a power attenuation proportional to frequency (i. e. -10 dB/decade) and if this is inserted before the analyzer input, the system can be calibrated as described for "bandwidth compensation". This is desirable in the case of analyzers which have a hyperbolic or other non-logarithmic frequency scale, since it is not then so simple to draw lines of constant PSD.

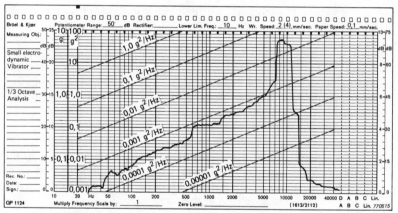

Fig.3.43. Typical 1/3-octave power spectrum with lines of constant PSD

3.5.3. High Speed Analysis

It was mentioned in Section 3.4.4, that by recording in a digital memory at one speed and then playing back M times faster it was theoretically possible to analyze M times faster. Fig.3.44 illustrates a typical instrument setup based on this principle, which may be termed "high speed analysis". Even though it is generally not possible to attain the theoretical improvement, the analysis can usually be speeded up to the point that analysis time is no longer a dominant factor.

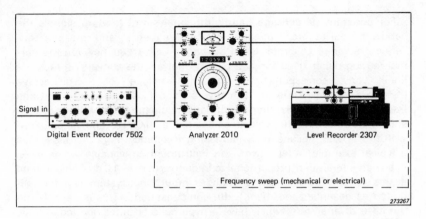

Signal in

Digital Event Recorder 7502 | Analyzer 2010 | Level Recorder 2307

Frequency sweep (mechanical or electrical)

273267

Fig.3.44. Typical instrument set-up for high speed analysis with Analyzer Type 2010 (constant bandwidth)

It is important to recognize the limitations introduced by the Digital Event Recorder, viz.

(1) The sampling of the time signal limits the frequency range to a maximum of $1/2$ the sampling frequency, and in practice with the Digital Event Recorder Type 7502 to $1/4$ the sampling frequency in order to avoid aliasing (Section 2.2.4). Lowpass filters are built in for each sampling frequency to ensure this.

(2) Taking a sample of length T (equal to the memory circulation time of the Digital Event Recorder) is the same as multiplying the endless signal with a rectangular function of length T, and as shown in Section 2.5.3 this corresponds to a convolution of the spectrum with the spectrum of the rectangular function.

(3) Repetitive playback of this signal sample with repetition period T_{rep} results in the formation of an artificially periodic signal, with a spectrum sampled at intervals of $1/T_{rep}$ (see Fig.2.28). With the Digital Event Recorder Type 7502, it is possible to make T_{rep} an integer multiple of T between 1 and 9. It will be found, however, that there is little benefit in making the ratio greater than 1.

As a matter of interest Fig.3.45 shows the effect of (2) and (3) in the particular case where the signal is sinusoidal and $T_{rep} = T$. The two extreme cases are shown, representing the cases where the spectrum is sampled:

106

(a)   at the peaks of the sidelobes

(b)   at the zeroes between the sidelobes (which is possible since the sidelobe width $1/T$ is equal to the sample spacing $1/T_{rep}$).

It will be found that (b) corresponds to the cases where there is an integer number of periods in the memory length, whereby the resulting signal is indistinguishable from a continuous sine wave and thus has only one component (as shown in Fig.3.45(b)). In practice, however, it is normally not possible to arrange for there to be an exact number of periods in the record length (remembering that there will normally be several hundred or even thousand periods), and thus it is advisable to allow for the worst case, by assuming the continuous basic spectrum. The average case will in fact give a result which is only 3 dB lower.

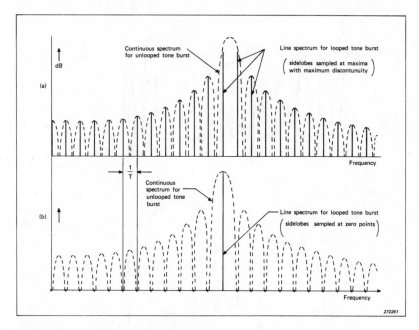

Fig.3.45. Line spectra for looped tone bursts obtained from corresponding continuous spectra

In order to counteract the discrete nature of the spectrum it is necessary to employ an analyzer bandwidth which is equal to or greater than the line spacing. This is in any case desirable for the following reasons:

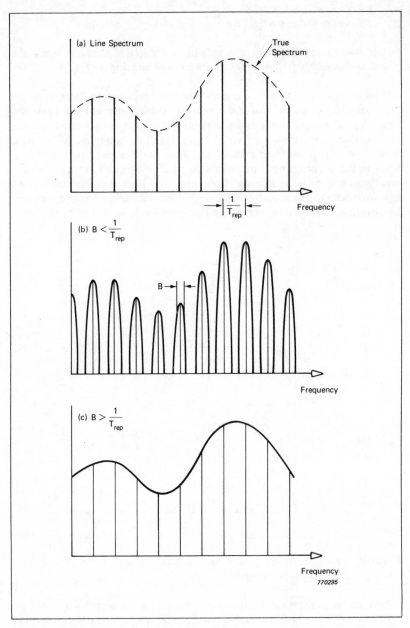

Fig.3.46. Effect of filter bandwidth when analyzing a line spectrum

(1) With an analyzer bandwidth less than the line spacing $1/T_{rep}$, the measured spectrum consists of peaks which are difficult to distinguish from actual peaks in the true spectrum (Fig.3.46(b)). Use of a bandwidth $B \geqslant 1/T_{rep}$ makes the measured spectrum continuous again, so that the true peaks can be easily distinguished (Fig.3.46(c)).

(2) The bandwidth of the results is in any case limited to a minimum equal to the reciprocal of the record length (i. e. $1/T$), and so use of a narrower analyzer bandwidth requires a longer analysis time without giving any more information.

Assuming the "worst case" situation then, it is necessary to determine what the effect will be of the convolution mentioned previously. Even though it is the complex spectra which are convolved, it will be found that the power spectra can also be considered as convolved, even though this is not strictly true (c. f. the discussion on this point at the end of Section 2.5.3).

In the case of a **deterministic** signal, provided the separation of the closest components is appreciably greater than the reciprocal of the record length (this is the same as saying that the record length includes several periods of the lowest beat frequency) then the situation will typically be as shown in Fig.3.47. In Fig.3.47(a) it is seen that each of the sinuoidal components has been separately convolved with the $(sin\ x)/x$ spectrum of the rectangular window•, but because they are reasonably well separated, it is only at some intermediate frequency (where the amplitudes are of the same magnitude) that there is any significant interaction. The height of each peak will be virtually unchanged (in the power spectrum also) and it is only in the valleys that significant differences can occur (depending on the phase relationships). Fig.3.47(b) illustrates the limiting cases where the adjacent sinusoidal components are in-phase and out-of-phase, and also the average situation corresponding to the convolution of the power spectra. It is important to realise that in the spectrum of a deterministic signal it is only the peaks which are important, while the valleys are determined by extraneous factors such as the filter characteristic.

In the case of a **random** signal, the phase is in any case random, and even after modification by the window function, the integration over a finite frequency band will tend to a limit corresponding to an integra-

---

• Note that only the main lobe of the $(sinx)/x$ function has been shown, not the sidelobes, so as not to confuse the picture. In fact, all of the sidelobes interact as well

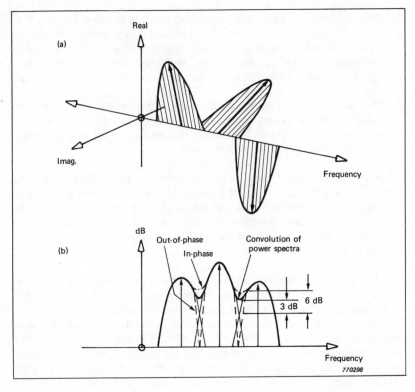

Fig.3.47. Interaction of adjacent discrete components

tion of mean square amplitudes, which in turn corresponds to the convolution of the power spectra. Thus the convolution of the power spectra gives the best estimate of the power spectrum of the convolution.

It remains to be seen what the effect is of a subsequent swept filtration with a practical filter, and this has been considered in some detail in Ref.3.4. There it is shown that the result corresponds to a further convolution with the power spectrum of the practical filter used, so that the overall filter function with which the original spectrum is filtered is the convolution of the power spectrum of the rectangular window with the power spectrum of the practical filter. In Ref.3.4 approximate results are derived for convolution with an ideal filter of bandwidth B as illustrated in Fig.3.48. These results correspond well with practical measurements provided the selectivity of the practical filter is some-

110

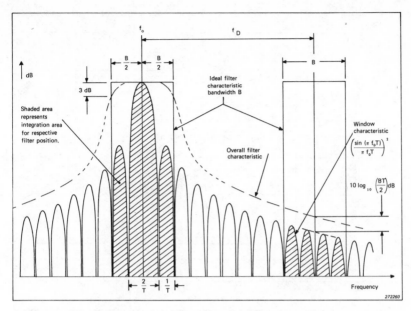

Fig.3.48. Determination of overall filter characteristic for rectangular window and ideal filter

what better than that of the convolution product (so that by comparison it could be considered as an ideal filter). The results from Ref.3.4 are expressed in graphical form in Figs.3.49 and 3.50. Fig.3.49 corresponds to constant bandwidth analysis and expresses the 40 dB Shape Factor of the "overall filter characteristic". Fig.3.50 applies to constant percentage bandwidth analysis, and expresses the octave selectivity of the "overall filter characteristic". Some examples should help to clarify the use of the graphs, and also give an idea of how serious the limitation on selectivity is. Assuming the Digital Event Recorder Type 7502 with 10K memory (10240 words) played back at a sample rate of 500k Samples/s (i. e. maximum valid frequency 125 kHz) the memory length T corresponds to approximately 20 ms, and the line spacing $1/T$ to 50 Hz. Choosing then a bandwidth of 316 Hz (> 50 Hz) it is found from Fig.3.49 that the 40 dB Shape Factor is 18. Fig.3.51(b) compares a high speed analysis corresponding to these conditions with the direct analysis in Fig.3.51(a), and indicates that the broadening of the base of the filter characteristic is not too serious a limitation where the record length can be made fairly long, as in this case. Where the broadening cannot be accepted, then use can be made of a smoother window function, e. g. of gaussian or cos² shape, to obtain a better frequency char-

111

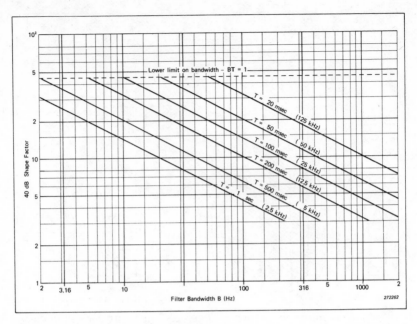

Fig.3.49. 40 dB shape factor for rectangular window length T and ideal filter bandwidth B

acteristic. Fig.3.51(c) shows the results of a high speed analysis using a gaussian window, and it will be seen that these are virtually the same as obtained in the direct analysis. However, the use of special weighting functions is more appropriate in the analysis of non-stationary signals (where the signal sample cannot be chosen arbitrarily long) and is treated in detail in Section 3.6.

It is worth remarking on the special considerations which apply in the case of constant percentage bandwidth analysis, at least over a wide frequency range. From the previous discussion, it is evident that the taking of a finite record of length T inherently gives a constant bandwidth spectrum, which automatically limits the frequency range. It will in fact be found that it is best to record and analyze separately for each decade in frequency. A practical example should help to make this clear:

In the Digital Event Recorder Type 7502 with 10K memory, the memory length includes approximately 2500 periods of the highest valid frequency. One decade lower in frequency represents 250 periods. From Equation (3.2) it will be appreciated that the minimum relative

112

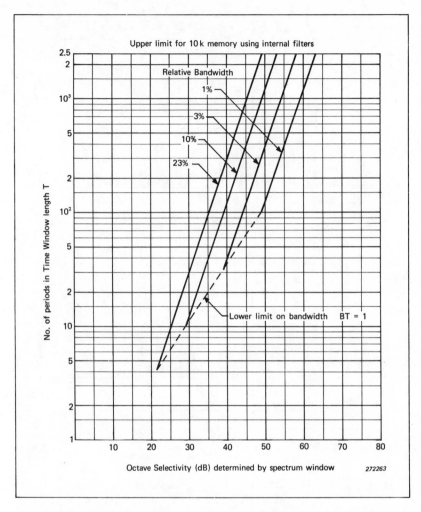

Fig.3.50. Octave selectivity for rectangular window length T and constant percentage bandwidth ideal filters

bandwidth in that case is $1/250 = 0,4\%$ and that this corresponds to a *BT* product of 1. A *BT* product of 10 would require a bandwidth of 4%. One decade lower again the corresponding bandwidths are 4% and 40% respectively. Moreover, from Fig.3.50 it will be seen that 250 periods corresponds to an octave selectivity of 43 dB (for 10% bandwidth) while 25 periods gives only 33 dB and in fact it is a general rule that

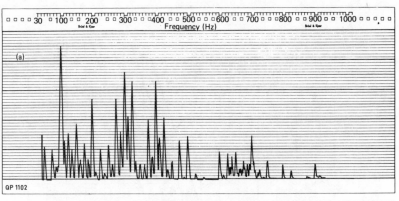

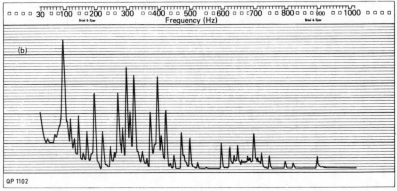

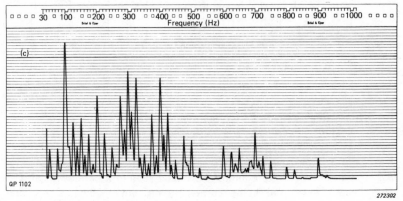

272302

Fig.3.51. (a) Normal swept analysis
        (b) High speed analysis with rectangular window (10K)
        (c) High speed analysis with gaussian window

the octave selectivity is 10 dB poorer for each decade lower in frequency.

A general guide to the selection of analysis parameters will now be given.

3.5.3.1. Choice of Sample Rate During Recording

It is evident from the previous discussion that the digital memory should contain as many periods as possible of the highest frequency of interest.

For **constant bandwidth** analysis, this will be achieved if the sampling rate is chosen as the lowest which still retains the highest frequency of interest. For example, with the Digital Event Recorder Type 7502, whose antialiasing filters cut off at $1/4$ the sampling frequency (f_s), the optimum sample rate during recording can be obtained by multiplying the maximum frequency of interest ($f_{max.}$) by 4 and then selecting the next highest value of sample rate. As an example, for $f_{max.}$ = 1 kHz, f_s must be selected $\geqslant 4$ kHz, and the next highest is thus 5k Samples/s (in a 2, 5, 10 sequence).

For **constant percentage bandwidth** analysis the same applies for each decade in frequency, and for example to analyze from 2 Hz to 2 kHz, it is first necessary to consider the decade 2 Hz to 20 Hz, giving a sample rate $f_s \geqslant 4 \times 20 = 100$ Samples/s. For the two higher decades the sample rates would be 1000 and 10000 Samples/s respectively.

3.5.3.2. Choice of Sample Rate During Playback

As a general rule, the sample rate during playback should be the maximum permitted by the Digital Event Recorder or the analyzer.

For **constant bandwidth** analysis this will typically be 500k Samples/s ($f_{max.}$ = 125 kHz) provided the analyzer frequency range is $\geqslant 125$ kHz. If the analyzer range is limited to 20 kHz, the playback rate will typically be limited to 100 k S/s ($f_{max.}$ = 25 kHz) and then only 80% of the valid frequency range during recording may be achieved. In some cases it may be desired to further limit the speed-up ratio to an even number of decades in order that the equivalent bandwidth of the

115

measured result is the same as that for a direct analysis. Where the analyzer bandwidths are in a $\sqrt{10}$, 10 sequence, these will only correspond with the 2, 5, 10 sequence of sample rates at even decade intervals. For example, if the sample rate during recording were 20 kS/s, then the sample rate during playback would be chosen as 200 kS/s (instead of 500 kS/s) so that the same equivalent bandwidth would be achieved with an actual bandwidth 10 times greater. The analysis time is evidently increased, however.

3.5.3.3. Choice of Memory Length

For **deterministic** signals the memory length must in any case be chosen $\geqslant$ the reciprocal of the desired bandwidth

i. e. $$T \geqslant \frac{1}{B} \qquad (3.24)$$

It is also necessary to take account of the selectivity (Fig.3.49) in cases where no special time window is used.

For **random** signals it will generally be the record length which limits the statistical accuracy of the results and thus T must be chosen such that:

$$T \geqslant \frac{K}{B} \qquad (3.25)$$

where K is the desired BT product for insertion in Equation (3.9) (or Table 3.4) with record length T replacing averaging time T_A.

3.5.3.4. Averaging Time T_A

As discussed in Section 3.5.1.1, the looped signal can be considered as a continuous signal on which is superimposed a series of impulses corresponding to the discontinuity at the end of the memory length, and thus repeated at intervals equal to the memory circulation time. Fourier analysis indicates that the effect of the discontinuity is to broaden the base of the filter characteristic without influencing the peaks. However, all information about the broadened characteristic is contained in the series of discontinuities, and the theoretical results assume an infinite integration time (or in practical terms an averaging time equal to several times the memory circulation time).

116

If the averaging time is made less than the record length (which may be valid for the continuous part of the signal) the discontinuities will result in fluctuations about the theoretical mean value, although the spectrum of the continuous signal provides a lower limit to the fluctuations (Fig.3.52). In Ref.3.5 it is shown how use can be made of this effect to reduce the window function effect when the spectrum is being digitised (using a trigger signal synchronous with the memory junction point to trigger the digitalisation).

Normally, however, these fluctuations would be disadvantageous, as they could be confused with actual spectrum peaks, and it is better to choose T_A a number of times longer than the memory circulation time, even though this introduces an inefficiency with respect to analysis speed. Normally it is best to start with an averaging time given by:

$$T_A \geqslant 3T \tag{3.26}$$

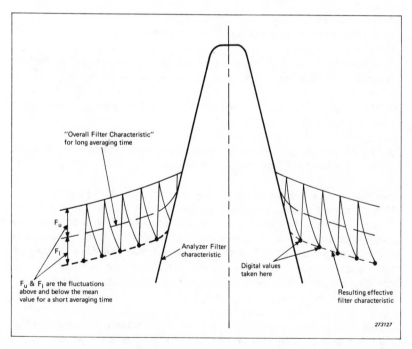

Fig.3.52. Overall filter characteristic

117

even though Fig.3.16 indicates that the fluctuation range will then be approx. 3 dB. The actual fluctuation is normally less, since for a deterministic signal Equation (3.24) indicates that the filter response time is typically of the order of the memory length and thus the pulses are "spread out" over this time. For a random signal, it is rarely that the true spectrum is steeper than the filter characteristic, so that the fluctuations will rarely be seen.

On the very few occasions that Eqn. (3.26) gives too great a fluctuation, this can be seen by inspection and the averaging time increased by one step.

3.5.3.5. Analysis Speed

The choice of dwell time T_D, and thus paper speed, should be based on the averaging time T_A, exactly as discussed in Sections 3.5.2.5 and 3.5.2.7.

3.5.4. Real-time Analysis (Time Compression)

The spectrum obtained from a time compression analyzer is subject to exactly the same limitations as a high speed analysis in that:

(1) The original time signal has been sampled , thus limiting the upper frequency.

(2) The record length is finite, thus giving both a discrete spectrum and a rectangular time window function.

Moreover, the memory length typically includes 400 periods of the highest frequency (compared with 2500 for a typical digital event recorder) so that the effect of the rectangular time window is considerably greater. For this reason a $\cos^2$ (Hanning) weighting function is generally included as standard and should normally be used for the analysis of stationary signals. As shown in Section 3.6, however, although the filter characteristic is improved as a whole, the noise bandwidth is increased by 50%.

Even though the operation of a time compression analyzer is relatively simple, it is still necessary to consider the following factors:

118

3.5.4.1. Bandwidth

With a rectangular weighting function, the bandwidth is equal to the line spacing (or spectrum resolution) which will be termed β. This is evidently equal to the selected frequency range divided by the number of lines. Moreover, since the Discrete Fourier Transform applies, the line spacing β is equal to the reciprocal of the record length T. Thus for each spectrum the BT product = $(1/T)\,T = 1$. In fact the same also applies when the time signal is weighted by a Hanning or other weighting function, since although the bandwidth is increased, the effective record length is reduced correspondingly (Ref.3.6).

As mentioned previously, when a Hanning weighting function is used the noise bandwidth = $1,5\beta$. Since the analyzer is calibrated for sinusoids, the measured power spectrum for random signals will be correspondingly greater when the Hanning window is used, viz. $10\log_{10}(1,5) = 1,8\,dB$.

P.S.D.s can be calculated by dividing the measured power spectrum values by the bandwidth (β and $1,5\beta$ for rectangular and Hanning windows respectively).

3.5.4.2. Averaging Time

Even though the BT product corresponding to each spectrum is 1, it is possible to increase the overall BT product by averaging over several independent spectra (thus effectively increasing T). This contrasts with high speed analysis (Section 3.5.3) where it was necessary to integrate over several frequency lines (thus increasing B).

The final BT product is then equal to the number of spectra averaged, and for example with the B & K Type 3348 this can be chosen between 8 and 1024 in binary steps. The averager is programmed to take in only independent spectra (i. e. at intervals of $1/\beta$, see Fig.3.53). Since each spectrum in itself represents an average over a time corresponding to the analyzer memory length, then averaging over these discrete spectra in fact represents an average over the total time. The effective number of spectra averaged may be inserted (instead of BT_A) in Equation (3.9) or Table 3.4, in order to obtain the standard error of the results for random signals.

The averaging can be carried out with a uniform (linear) weighting on

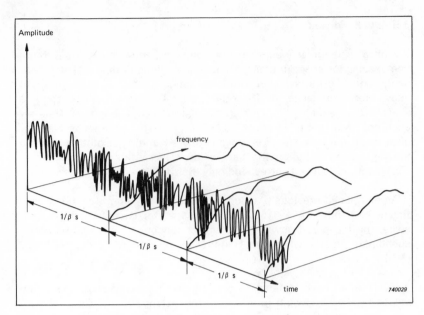

Fig.3.53. Spectrum sampling at intervals of 1/β

each spectrum, whereafter it is normally necessary to hold the result (thus ignoring the continuation of the signal), but for continuous monitoring it is possible to obtain a continuously updated result with exponential weighting analogous to analog RC-averaging. An example may help to clarify the way in which this is achieved:

If 10% of each new spectrum is added to 90% of the current result, then the total is given by

$$0,1S_n + 0,1(0,9)S_{n-1} + 0,1(0,9)^2 S_{n-2} + \cdots\cdots\cdots\cdots$$

which will be seen to comprise an exponentially decaying series of weighting factors as illustrated in Fig.3.54. The effective averaging time is dependent on the relative proportions of old and new spectra added together (in this case 0,9 and 0,1) and by comparing Fig.3.54 with Fig.3.14 it will be seen that the RC time constant in this case will be approximately 10 sample periods and the effective averaging time twice this, or 20 sample periods. Using the relative proportions 0,99 and 0,01 would give an averaging time which is 10 times longer.

The simple recursive algorithm just described is in fact one example

120

of a digital filter (a single-pole RC lowpass filter) and this example will
be taken up again in Chapter 5 (Digital Filters).

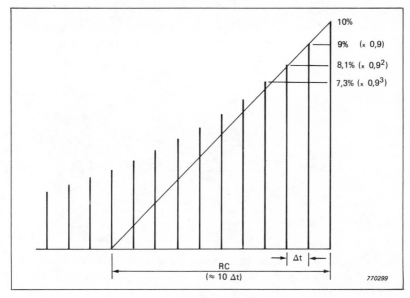

Fig.3.54. Weighting of various samples for digital exponential averaging

3.6. PRACTICAL ANALYSIS OF CONTINUOUS NON-STATIONARY SIGNALS

As illustrated in Fig.2.25, it is possible to move a time window along
a non-stationary signal and obtain the frequency spectrum of each windowed section. The individual spectra can then be placed into a 3-di-
mensional diagram (e. g. Fig.3.55) to see the development of the frequency spectrum with time. However, it is important to realise the limitations imposed by the window function on the validity of results obtained in that way.

The effect of simply cutting off the signal except for a length T (i. e.
using a rectangular window of length T) was first discussed in
Section 2.5.3, where it was shown that the effect on the spectrum is
to convolve it with the spectrum of the rectangular window function. In
Section 3.5 the effect on the overall filter characteristic of a further fil-

121

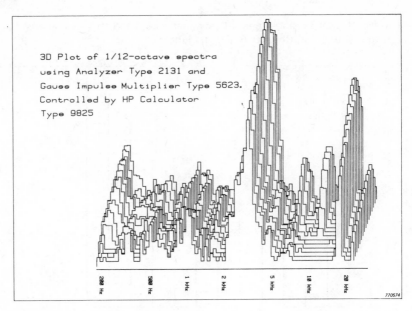

Fig.3.55. A 3-dimensional plot showing the development of the frequency spectrum with time

tration by a practical filter was discussed in some detail. The problems with a rectangular window arise from the sudden transitions at each end, which in general result in a discontinuity when the signal sample is joined into a loop (Fig.3.56(a)). Use of a smoother weighting function, for example of gaussian shape (Fig.3.56(b)) nullifies the discontinuity (Fig.3.56(c)) and might thus be expected to give a better result. It can be seen that any function other than a rectangle will give a different weighting to different parts of the signal sample, but for stationary signals at least, this should not give any problems since the relative proportions of the various frequency components will be the same along the whole record. For non-stationary signals the signal sample will often be chosen sufficiently short that it is effectively stationary. In any case the steps with which the window is moved can be made so short that each section will be adequately emphasized in one or other of the analyses.

The influence of the weighting function can best be judged in the frequency domain, however, and Fig.3.57 illustrates this for the rectangular and gaussian windows of Fig.3.56 (now applied to a single sinusoidal signal). The gaussian function is typical of many smooth weight-

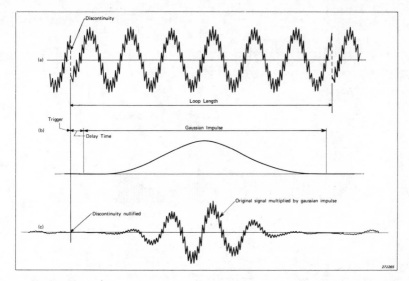

Fig.3.56. Effect on the junction discontinuity of a gaussian window (time domain)

ing functions in that it gives greatly improved selectivity, while increasing the bandwidth somewhat.

In general, when making an analysis of a non-stationary signal it will be necessary to consider the following factors:

(1) Choice of window type
(2) Choice of window length
(3) Choice of incremental steps
(4) Practical details
(5) Scaling of results

3.6.1. Choice of Window Type

As mentioned, the comparison can best be made in the frequency domain, and Fig.3.58 compares the spectra (one-sided spectra on log-log scales) of the following commonly used window functions:

(1) A rectangular window of length T
(2) A **Hanning** (cosine^2) window
(3) A **Hamming** window (Hanning on a small rectangular pedestal)

123

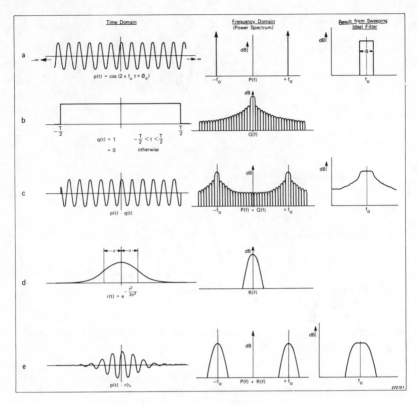

Fig.3.57. Comparison of rectangular and gaussian windows in time and frequency domains
(a) Infinite sinusoid
(b) Rectangular weighting function .
(c) Sinusoid weighted with a rectangular function
(d) Gaussian weighting function
(e) Sinusoid weighted with a gaussian function

(4) A gaussian window

* These are all compared on the basis of having the same total length T. For the gaussian function (which is theoretically infinitely long) this has been interpreted as 3 times the half amplitude length T_G (see Fig.3.59), i.e. 7,06 times the standard deviation σ, since the truncation then has no effect over a dynamic range of 65 dB or so.

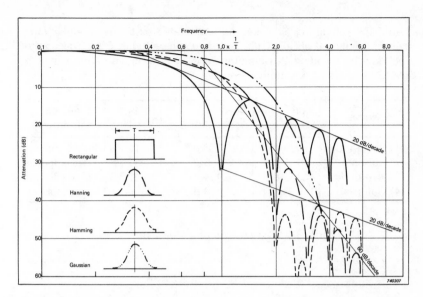

Fig.3.58. Comparison of the spectra of some common time window functions

Table 3.7 compares the window functions of Fig.3.58 with respect to the following parameters:

(1) 3 dB and effective noise bandwidth
(2) Height of maximum sidelobe
(3) Rate of fall-off of sidelobes

It is found that the Hanning function gives very good results compared with the rectangular and is thus commonly used since it is easily generated. In time compression analyzers, for example, sinusoidal signals synchronous with the memory circulation time are available and can be used to weight the signal. In FFT analyzers (see Chapter 5) a table of sine/cosine values is normally available (for use in the FFT algorithm) and can be utilised for generating a Hanning window.

The Hamming window is obtained by mounting a Hanning window on a small rectangular pedestal. It will be seen from Fig.3.58 that the second sidelobe of the rectangular function coincides with the first sidelobe of the Hanning function, and since it has opposite phase, it can be made (by appropriate scaling) to cancel the highest sidelobe of the Hanning function so that the highest is then 10 dB lower. On the other

125

hand, the remaining sidelobes are dominated by the rectangular function and only fall off at 20 dB/decade compared with 60 dB/decade for
the Hanning window. A Hamming window is of course almost as simple to generate as a Hanning window.

Name	3 dB Bandwidth	Noise Bandwidth B_{eff}	Highest Sidelobe	Sidelobe fall-off rate
(1) Rectangular	0,9 β ●	1,0 β ●	—13 dB	20 dB/decade
(2) Hanning	1,4 β	1,5 β	—32 dB	60 dB/decade
(3) Hamming	1,3 β	1,4 β	—42 dB	20 dB/decade
(4) Gaussian	1,8 β	1,9 β	None	No sidelobes

● N.B. $\beta = 1/T$

Table 3.7. Comparison of window functions

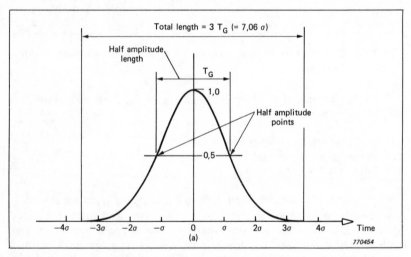

*Fig.3.59. Gaussian time window in terms of standard deviation σ and
half amplitude length T_G*

The gaussian function has the property of transforming by the Fourier
transform to another gaussian function. Since it is of the general form
e^{-x^2} (see Section 2.4.2), on a logarithmic amplitude (i. e. dB) scale it
becomes an inverted parabola with no sidelobes and a characteristic
which becomes successively steeper. From this point of view it is ideal,
but on the other hand its bandwidth is greater than that of the other

126

types shown. For analog analysis, where there are not the same restric-' tions on the overall length of signal sample as in finite digital memories, the gaussian window is probably the best choice. Moreover, if the window has to be generated at some arbitrary point in time, then it is no more difficult to make it gaussian than sinusoidal (oscillators take a certain time to respond).

3.6.2. Choice of Window Length

As a general rule, the window length should always be made as long as possible, but will normally be limited by how rapidly the signal itself is changing. In speech, for example, it is typical for individual sounds to last 40 ms or so and this is a typical window length to choose. The limitation on making it too short is of course that the shorter the time scaling, the larger is the bandwidth. The effective length T_E of the various window types (for comparison purposes) can in fact be taken to be the reciprocal of the noise bandwidth as given in Table 3.7, i. e.

$$T_E = \frac{1}{B_{eff}} \qquad (3.27)$$

This value of T_E can be used to replace T_A in Eqn.3.9 (or Table 3.4) in cases where the windowed signal sample is of random character and relatively stationary. The analyzer bandwidth must in that case be several times greater than that of the window function, as the BT product will be given by this ratio.

It is worth remarking that with constant percentage bandwidth analysis over a wide frequency range, there will be a certain frequency below which the bandwidth of the results is determined by the window function, rather than by the analyzer bandwidth. An example should help to illustrate this. If speech is analyzed with a gaussian window of half amplitude length $T_G = 20$ ms the total length $T = 3T_G = 60$ ms and from Table 3.7 the noise bandwidth will thus be $1,9/0,06 = 32$ Hz. If the windowed sample is then analyzed with 1/3-octave bandwidth (23,1%) the analyzer bandwidth will be less than that of the window for all frequencies less than $32/0,231 = 138$ Hz i. e. all 1/3-octave bands from 125 Hz and downwards.

It is also worth remarking that the bandwidth in itself sets a limit to the lowest frequency for which the results are at all valid. In the above example it was thus 32 Hz.

127

3.6.3. Choice of Incremental Step

It is natural to base the incremental steps between analyses on the effective length T_E as defined in Eqn.(3.27). If the step is made equal to T_E, then successive analyses will be effectively non-correlated, but in general it is desirable to make the steps somewhat shorter so that there is a certain amount of redundant information in successive analyses. This should assist in visualising the development with time.

As an example, with a Hanning window the effective bandwidth (from Table 3.7) is *1,5β* and so from Eqn.(3.27) the effective length T_E is *0,67 T*. An incremental step equal to *0,5 T* is thus a good choice in this case.

3.6.4. Practical Details

By this is meant the choice of analysis parameters such as analyzer bandwidth, and the utilisation of an intermediate recording memory.

From the point of view of analysis speed, the analyzer **bandwidth** should as usual be made as large as is compatible with the required resolution of the results. If the allowable bandwidth is greater than that determined by the window (Table 3.7) then no special remarks are required, and the effects of the window will not be apparent in the results. Where it is desired to get the best resolution possible from a given window length, then the analyzer bandwidth may be made narrower than that given by the window (say 1/2 or 1/3 the width) although this is of course inefficient from the point of view of analysis speed. It should be ensured that the analyzer bandwidth is at least equal to the separation of the spectral lines determined by the overall record length (if necessary the latter can be increased with blank record as discussed in Section 3.7.1.1 in association with Fig.3.65). Another factor to be taken into account is that of the selectivity of the analyzer filter compared with that of the window. Where a gaussian window is used, the selectivity is likely to be considerably better than that of the practical filter used, and this may necessitate the choice of a narrower analyzer bandwidth. (Fig.3.60).

Where the signal is to be recorded in a digital memory such as a Digital Event Recorder prior to analysis (e. g. in order to reduce analysis time) it is important that the memory be utilised efficiently. As a general rule, the window should always occupy as much of the memory as

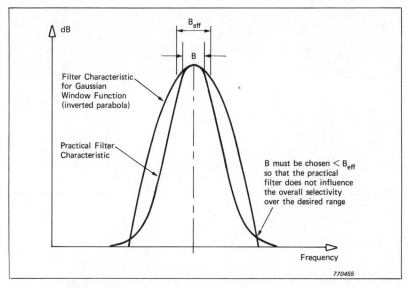

Fig.3.60. Choice of practical filter bandwidth so as not to reduce selectivity due to gaussian window

possible for the following reasons:

1) As explained in Section 3.5.3.1 (for rectangular weighting) the upper frequency is limited by the sampling frequency while the lower frequency is limited by the bandwidth (which in turn is limited by the window length). Thus for the same sample rate, a reduction of the window length to, for example, 1/10 reduces the valid frequency range by one decade.

2) The shorter the effective window length for a given repetition time, the more will be the limitation of dynamic range and the greater will be the problems due to crest factor.

Fig.3.61 illustrates how a window function can be moved along a time signal (assumed to be recorded on tape) while at the same time it occupies as much as possible of the digital memory used to speed up the analysis.

All other analysis parameters may be chosen by treating the windowed signal sample as a transient and analyzing as described in Section 3.7. Only the scaling of the results will be different.

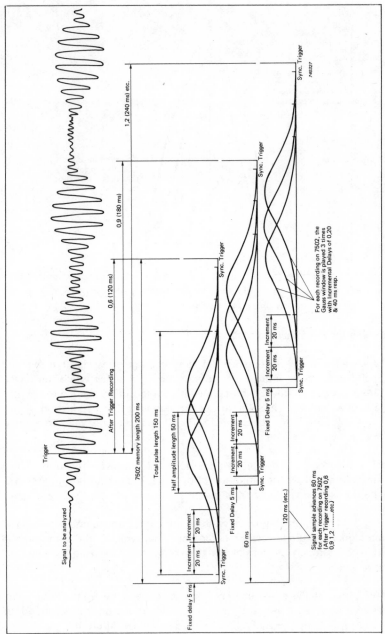

Fig. 3.61. Efficient means of moving the time window along the signal

130

3.6.5. Scaling of the Results

When a weighting function is used to take a sample from a continuous record, the sample in question is a transient with a finite energy content, but it will normally be desired to obtain the results in terms of the power of the equivalent stationary function having the same strength as the centre portion of the windowed sample (where the value of the weighting function is greatest).

The simplest and best way of determining the effect of a weighting function is to apply it to a reference signal and then compare all later practical measurements to this as described in Section 3.5.2.9.

It is possible, however, to calculate the effect as follows:

If the weighting function $W(t)$ is assumed to have a maximum value of unity and a length of T over which its value is non-zero, then what is required is the factor by which the energy of a windowed sample is reduced in comparison with a uniform weighting of unit value over length T (see Fig.3.62). Assuming that the stationary signal to which the windows are applied is $g(t)$, then its instantaneous power is $\{g(t)\}^2$ and that of the weighted signal is $\{W(t) \cdot g(t)\}^2 = \{W(t)\}^2 \cdot \{g(t)\}^2$. Provided $W(t)$ is only slowly varying over times for which $g(t)$ may be considered stationary (and thus for which the short term average of $\{g(t)\}^2$ is approximately constant) the total factor by with the **energy** is reduced is given by:

$$F_a = \frac{1}{T} \int_{-T/2}^{T/2} \{W(t)\}^2 \, dt \qquad (3.28)$$

The attenuation factor in dB is given by $10 \log_{10} [F_a]$.

It may help to give an example of the use of Eqn.(3.28), and the case will be taken of a gaussian window. The basic formula for a gaussian function centred on zero (see Section 2.4.2) is:

$$X(t) = \frac{1}{\sigma\sqrt{2\pi}} \exp\left(-\frac{t^2}{2\sigma^2}\right)$$

As explained in Section 2.4.2 the total integral over this function is 1, and thus if it is scaled to a maximum value of 1 (i.e. scaled up by the factor $\sigma\sqrt{2\pi}$) then the desired weighting function

131

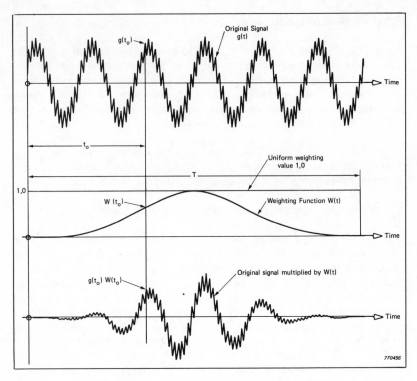

Fig.3.62. Effect of weighting function W(t)

$$W(t) = exp\left(-\frac{t^2}{2\sigma^2}\right) \qquad (3.29)$$

and the total integral will evidently be $\sigma\sqrt{2\pi}$. The square of $W(t)$ is also a gaussian function as follows:

$$\{W(t)\}^2 = exp\left(-\frac{2t^2}{2\sigma^2}\right)$$
$$= exp\left(-\frac{t^2}{2\sigma_1{}^2}\right) \qquad (3.30)$$

(where $\sigma_1 = \sigma/\sqrt{2}$)

and thus the total integral under this is $\sigma_1\sqrt{2\pi} = \sigma\sqrt{\pi}$

132

Fig.3.63 illustrates the linear and squared weighting functions.

For a total length $T = 3T_G = 7{,}06\sigma$, the attenuation factor:

$$F_a = \frac{1}{T} \int_{-T/2}^{T/2} \{W(t)\}^2 \, dt \approx \frac{\sigma\sqrt{\pi}}{7{,}06\,\sigma} = 0{,}25 \ (i.e. \ -6 \ dB)$$

Note that the value as calculated by Eqn.(3.28) applies only when the loop length (repetition time) is equal to T. If the repetition time is longer ($T_{rep} > T$) then in fact Eqn.(3.28) can still be used, replacing T by T_{rep}. The value of the integral will thereby be unchanged and thus F_a will be inversely proportional to the repetition time as required.

It is to be emphasized that F_a is a **power** attenuation factor, and thus a factor of 10 corresponds to a change of 10 dB or ratio of 3,16 in the RMS level. Moreover, F_a gives the reduction of total power content, and can thus be applied directly to power spectra, in particular those comprised of discrete frequency components. The same applies to Power Spectral Density measurements in the usual case where the analysis bandwidth is the same independent of whether or not a weighting

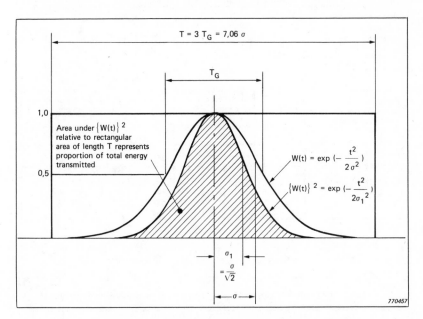

Fig.3.63. Energy transmitted by a gaussian window

133

function is used. Note that this contrasts with the case of analyzers based on the DFT (e. g. Time Compression and FFT analyzers) where the analysis bandwidth is determined by the window function, and where this bandwidth must be used in calculating PSD's. This has already been discussed for time compression analysis of stationary signals in Section 3.5.4.1.

3.7. PRACTICAL ANALYSIS OF TRANSIENTS

A number of methods are available for the analog analysis of transients, but the choice between them is not entirely free. In general, for a particular set of circumstances, one method will be preferable.

Fig.3.64 indicates the fundamental breakdown into four separate analysis methods and at the same time the conditions for which each is applicable. The basic division is between the methods where the transient is played back repetitively and analyzed as a stationary (periodic) signal,

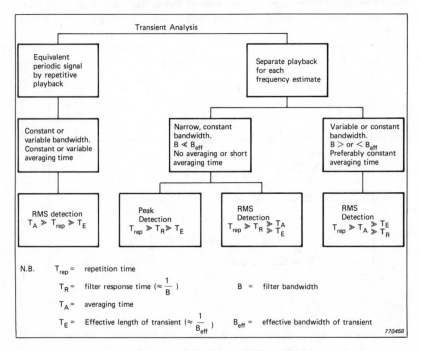

Fig.3.64. Methods of transient analysis

and the methods where a separate estimate is obtained for each passage of the transient and for each passage the filter is stepped or swept to a new frequency.

Each method will now be considered in some detail.

3.7.1. Analysis as a Periodic Signal

By this is meant the analysis of the signal formed by repetitive playback of the transient with a repetition time T_{rep} which is longer than the transient itself. In this way, the signal becomes artificially periodic, but as explained in Section 3.5.3 the resulting line spectrum can be related relatively simply to the true continuous spectrum. Moreover, the power spectrum units measured can be easily converted to energy by multiplying by the repetition time. In order to measure the power of the periodic signal, RMS detection must be used, with an averaging time T_A a number of times longer than the repetition time in order to damp out fluctuations.

In general, this is the best method to use for the following reasons:

1. Familiar analysis techniques for stationary signals can be used.

2. Within the limitations imposed by the bandwidth itself, the results are not very sensitive to the choice of bandwidth. For example, it is generally not necessary to take account of filter response time, and the choice between constant bandwidth and constant percentage bandwidth is free. It is necessary, however, to ensure that the bandwidth is always greater than the artificially introduced spectral line spacing.

3. Provided that the averaging time is sufficiently long to reduce fluctuations to an acceptable level, the results are not affected by a further increase in averaging time.

4. The scaling of the results is relatively simple and virtually independent of the particular analyzer used.

5. The spectrum obtained is continuous rather than a series of peaks.

On the other hand, where the effective length of the transient is short with respect to the repetition time (say, < 10%) there is a chance that it will not be possible to use this method for one of the following reasons:

1. The available dynamic range of the result is reduced in direct proportion to the ratio of repetition time to effective pulse length.

2. For detectors with a crest factor limitation, the crest factor of the looped signal may make the results invalid. Note that it is the crest factor of the filtered signal rather than the original signal which is important. For measuring amplifiers with both peak and RMS detectors, it is a simple matter to check the crest factor of the filtered signal as the ratio of these two values (see Section 3.2.1). For measuring amplifiers with only an RMS detector, the peak value should be measured on an oscilloscope. When the signal crest factor is within the allowable range, the crest factor derived in this way will be valid. When the crest factor is over the allowable, the indicated RMS level will be low and the calculated crest factor even higher than the actual. Thus, this is a sensitive test for the validity of the results with respect to crest factor.

Provided that the conditions on dynamic range and crest factor are met, it will be necessary to take account of the following factors:

3.7.1.1. Analyzer Bandwidth

The primary restriction on analyzer bandwidth is that it be greater than the Fourier line spacing, i.e .

$$B \geqslant \frac{1}{T_{rep}} \qquad (3.31)$$

where T_{rep} is the repetition time.

The justification for this is exactly the same as for high speed analysis of stationary signals as discussed in Section 3.5.3.

It may also be desired to employ an analyzer bandwidth somewhat narrower than the intrinsic bandwidth of the function itself; for example, in the case of a rectangular pulse (see Fig.2.24) it may be desired to demarcate the zeroes in the spectrum with a better resolution than that given by the bandwidth of the pulse itself. A typical choice of bandwidth in that case would be $1/5$ of the bandwidth B_{eff} (= $1/T_E$ where T_E is the length of the pulse) and this would require a repetition time T_{rep} at least 5 times T_E in order to satisfy Eqn.(3.31). It should be kept

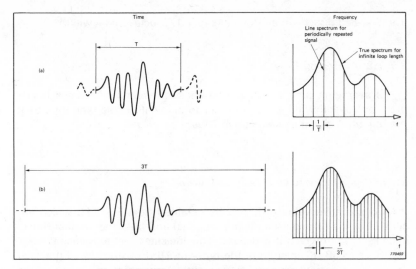

Fig.3.65. Effect of increasing repetition time
(a) Repetition time T
(b) Repetition time 3T

in mind that although it is possible to increase the repetition time to allow analysis with a narrower bandwidth (see Fig.3.65) this increases the likelihood of encountering problems with dynamic range and crest factor.

Another possible restriction on analyzer bandwidth applies to the cases where it is desired to express the results as an "energy spectral density". In that case the bandwidth must be less than that of the transient itself in order for the results to be valid, i.e .

$$B < B_{\text{eff}} \qquad (3.32)$$

The effective bandwidth B_{eff} can in general only be determined by analyzing the signal (for example using successively narrower bandwidths until the results remain unchanged) but since it is equal to the reciprocal of the effective length T_E, and as the latter can often be judged by eye with some experience, it will often be possible to arrive at suitable bandwidth with a minimum of trial and error.

Where Equation (3.32) is not fulfilled, and this will typically be the case with 1/3-octave spectra (where the bandwidth is fixed in advance), then it is not valid to express the results as an energy spectral density, but they will still be repeatable as a "1/3-octave energy spec-

137

trum" scaled directly in energy units (per 1/3-octave bandwidth).

3.7.1.2. Averaging Time

The averaging time T_A should be chosen a number of times longer than the repetition time T_{rep} in order to eliminate ripple (and thus treat the repetitive signal as stationary). Thus

$$T_A \geqslant KT_{rep} \qquad (3.33)$$

where K is a factor to be chosen as follows:

A conservative value of K can be obtained from Fig.3.16 which applies to trains of impulses (delta functions) and from the original Reference (3.1) from which it is derived. This indicates that to reduce the ripple to ± 1/4 dB, K must be of the order of 16. However, in all practical cases the transient extends over a certain time and K can be made smaller. When the filter bandwidth is just greater than the Fourier line spacing (Eqn.3.31) the filter response time T_R will be of the order of the repetition time T_{rep} , and then there will be sufficient overlapping of successive filter responses that a factor of 3 will often be sufficient. It is probably adivsable to start with a factor $K \geqslant 3$ and then increase it if found necessary by visual inspection.

3.7.1.3. Sweep Speed

Once the averaging time T_A has been decided, the dwell time T_D and thus sweep speed can be selected in exactly the same way as described for stationary signals in Sections 3.5.1.4, 3.5.2.5, 3.5.2.7 and 3.5.2.8. Note that provided the crest factor limitations of the Level Recorder are not exceeded, it is even possible to use AC recording.

3.7.1.4. Calibration of Results

Once the analysis is calibrated as a power spectrum (e. g. V^2) or power spectral density (e. g. V^2/Hz) as described in Section 3.5.2.9, it can be converted into an energy spectrum or energy spectral density, respectively, by multiplying by the repetition time T_{rep} . The reason for this is that the mean power of the repeated signal is evidently equal to the energy contained in one transient divided by the repetition time.

138

This calibration method also applies to a time compression analyzer where the transient is captured in the analyzer memory.

3.7.2. Analysis by Repeated Playback (Narrow Constant Bandwidth)

When it is not possible to make the repetition time sufficiently short to avoid problems with dynamic range and/or crest factor, it is necessary to utilize another method whereby the analysis at each frequency is obtained from the response of a filter (tuned to that frequency) to a single application of the transient. The complete analysis can then be obtained by stepping or sweeping the filter over a frequency range. Fig.3.66 illustrates an analysis obtained in this way. The true analysis is to be interpreted as the envelope of the individual peaks.

As indicated in Fig.3.64 there is a further basic division depending on whether the filter bandwidth is always less than that of the transient. It is this which is meant by the term "narrow constant bandwidth" and which is treated in this section.

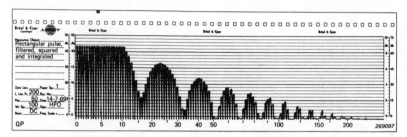

Fig.3.66. Typical impulse analysis where the result is given by the envelope curve

This method will typically be applicable to the case where the analyzer bandwidth is chosen as, say, 1/5 of the bandwidth of the function being analyzed, which is the same as saying that the filter response time is about 5 times longer than the transient. This being the case, the filter response is effectively equal to its impulse response, i. e. relatively insensitive to the actual shape of the transient and dependent only on its energy content around the frequency in question. In Ref.3.7 it is shown that there is a simple relationship between the spectral component and the peak value of the filter response, and thus it can be measured using a peak detector. For analyzers having only an RMS detector it is also possible to use that with an appropriately short averag-

139

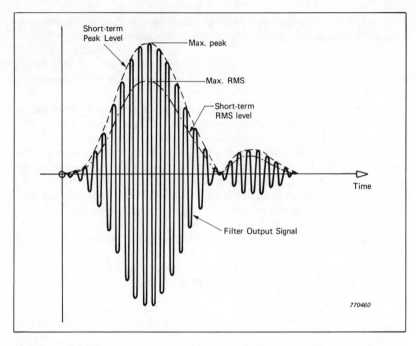

Fig.3.67. Short-term RMS and peak levels for a filter output pulse

ing time such that its output follows the envelope of the filter response and can thus be scaled up appropriately to obtain the equivalent peak value (see Fig.3.67).

The choice of the various parameters will now be considered in some detail.

3.7.2.1 Analyzer Bandwidth

As mentioned previously, the basic requirement is that the filter response time is appreciably longer than the effective length of the transient and this will be satisfied if:

$$B < \frac{1}{5T_E} \tag{3.34}$$

where T_E is the effective length of the transient.

140

T_E is defined as the reciprocal of B_{eff}, the effective bandwidth, but with some experience it can usually be estimated by eye with sufficient accuracy. A conservative estimate will always be obtained by setting it equal to the total length (the limiting case corresponding to a rectangular pulse or tone burst).

3.7.2.2. Detector Characteristics

In Ref.3.7 it is shown that the impulse response of an ideal filter of bandwidth B is as illustrated in Fig.3.68. The "envelope" of this function (which thus determines the peak value) is a *sin x/x* function with a lobe width determined by the filter bandwidth, while the sinusoidal fluctuations inside the envelope are at the tuned centre frequency of the filter (f_o). The filter response time t_L depends on the assumed phase characteristic, but in a practical case will generally be of the order of $1/B$ and thus shorter than illustrated.●

The peak level of the filter output (V_{peak}) was shown in Ref.3.7 to be equal to $2B|G(f_o)|$, where $|G(f_o)|$ is the modulus of the Fourier component at frequency f_o, and thus:

$$|G(f_0)| = \frac{V_{peak}}{2B} \tag{3.35}$$

Thus, the required Fourier component can be obtained using a *peak* detector which is reset in between successive playbacks. △

If a peak detector is not available, an RMS detector can also be used to obtain an indication of the peak value, provided that the averaging time fulfills the following requirements:

1. The averaging time must be large enough to reduce ripple due to the

---

● In Fig.3.68 a distinction is made between the total "lag time" t_L and the "rise time" T_R. In most practical cases, however, both will be of the order of $1/B$ and will both be referred to as the "response time T_R"

△ Note that with the B & K Measuring Amplifier Type 2607 it is possible to arrange for the peak detector to be reset between playbacks, and this will normally be the most efficient setup, but it is also possible to allow the detector to fall with a time constant determined by the set averaging time. The sweep speed will then be limited by this time constant, however, as though RMS detection had been used

filter ringing frequency f_0 •, and from Equation 3.15 this will be achieved if:

$$T_A \geqslant \frac{3}{f_0} \qquad (3.15)$$

2. The averaging time must be appreciably shorter than the filter response time so that the short-term RMS level follows the envelope of the filter response curve (though 3 dB lower than the peak value). This will be the case within about 1 dB for

$$T_A \leqslant \frac{1}{3B} \qquad (3.36)$$

Combining Equations (3.15) and (3.35) results in

$$\frac{1}{3B} \geqslant \frac{3}{f_0} \qquad (3.37)$$

$$\text{or} \quad f_0 \geqslant 9B$$

indicating that the RMS detector can only be used for frequencies greater than 9 or 10 times the filter bandwidth. This limitation does not apply to the Analyzer Type 2010, or others with a fixed filter output frequency (see footnote).

3.7.2.3. Repetition Time T_{rep}

Where peak detection is used, the major requirement is that the individual filter responses are adequately separated from each other. This will be the case if the repetition time is greater than twice the filter response time, i. e.

$$T_{\text{rep}} \geqslant \frac{2}{B} \qquad (3.38)$$

For very short repetition times, it should also be checked that the recorder writing speed does not limit the registration of the spectrum. The pen will be able to rise and fall over at least a 20 dB range if the following equation is satisfied:

• Note that with the B & K Analyzer Type 2010, the filter output frequency is constant (750 Hz or 30 kHz) independent of the filter centre frequency. The shortest averaging time (0,1 s) will therefore always damp out ripple

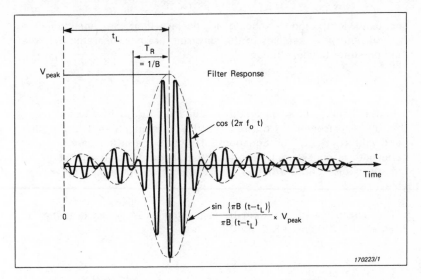

Fig.3.68. Impulse response of an ideal filter

$$T_{rep} \geqslant \frac{100}{W} \qquad (3.39)$$

where W is the writing speed corresponding to 100 mm paper.

As an example, for $W = 1000$ mm/s, the minimum value of T_{rep} is 0,1 s.

The above assumes that the peak detector is reset before each playback. If the rate of fall of the peak detector is determined by the selected averaging time, or if RMS detection is used, then the repetition time should be large enough that the RMS detector can fall more than about 20 dB between successive playbacks. Keeping in mind that the maximum rate of fall is 8,7 dB/averaging time (Fig.3.21) then the repetition time T_{rep} should **also** satisfy:

$$T_{rep} \geqslant 3T_A \qquad (3.40)$$

3.7.2.4. Sweep Speed

Once again defining the dwell time T_D as the time taken to sweep

143

one bandwidth, then T_D should not be less than the repetition time T_{rep} in order that samples of the spectrum are not separated by more than one filter bandwidth, i. e.

$$T_D \geqslant T_{rep} \qquad (3.41)$$

In the limiting case governed by Equation (3.38) this would mean that the displacement of the result could be as much as $1/2$ the filter bandwidth ($T_D \geqslant 2T_R$, cf. Equation 3.19) but since in this case the filter bandwidth is considerably less than the bandwidth of the function being measured (Eqn.3.34) this displacement will generally be acceptable.

The sweep speed can then be calculated as B/T_D as described in Sections 3.5.3.5 and 3.5.2.7.

3.7.2.5. Calibration of Results

Equation (3.35) indicates how the results can be calibrated for an ideal filter of bandwidth B. It should be noted that $|G(f_o)|$ is the modulus of the Fourier component at frequency f_o as given by Equation (2.14). It applies to the 2-sided spectrum, and its square gives the energy spectral density of the positive frequency component alone. Thus, in order to express the results in terms of RMS levels (c.f. Fig.2.5) the value $|G(f_o)|$ must be multiplied by $\sqrt{2}$ so that its square represents the total energy spectral density associated with frequency f_o (both positive and negative frequency contributions) i. e.

$$G_{RMS}(f_0) = \frac{V_{peak}}{\sqrt{2}B} \qquad (3.42)$$

The energy spectral density for comparison with results obtained as described in Section 3.7.1.4 is obtained by squaring $G_{RMS}(f_0)$.

In Ref.3.8 it is mentioned that equations (3.35) and (3.42) do not apply to practical filters in general, although they will be very close for filters with a good shape factor. It is possible, however, to establish a scaling factor for each filter by which the results from Equations (3.35) and (3.42) can be multiplied. The scaling factor can be obtained by analyzing a known signal such as a retangular pulse or tone burst.

Where short-term RMS detection is used, the result would in general

144

be 3 dB below the corresponding peak amplitude (provided $T_A \ll T_R$). In the limiting case determined by Eqn.(3.36) where the averaging time is $1/3$ the filter response time the short-term RMS value is about 4 dB below the peak value (see example in Section 2.7.4). Minor differences of this sort can also be calibrated out by analyzing a known signal, the factor obtained being valid for a given ratio of averaging time to filter response time (i. e. for a given BT_A product).

A word on dimensions is perhaps in order. The results of Equations (3.35) and (3.42) will have the dimensions Volts/Hz or Volt seconds. The squares of these will thus have the dimensions $V^2 s^2$ (i. e., $V^2 s$/Hz) and thus represent energy spectral density (power × time/unit frequency). Note that Equation (3.34) ensures that it is always valid to express the results as an energy spectral density.

3.7.3. Analysis by Repeated Playback (Variable Bandwidth)

The method described in Section 3.7.2 is limited by Equation (3.34) and is thus in practice virtually limited to narrow constant bandwidth analysis. It is however possible to make an analysis with for example constant percentage bandwidth, and in particular $1/3$ octave bandwidth, by using another approach. Independent of the filter bandwidth, the filter output pulse will always contain that part of the energy of the original transient which falls within the passband of the filter. It is thus possible to measure this energy with an RMS detector provided certain conditions are fulfilled. Basically, the averaging time must be longer than the pulse; for linearly weighted averaging, just longer, and for exponentially weighted averaging several times longer in order for the energy to be properly integrated. On the other hand, the crest factor and dynamic range limitations of the detector must not be exceeded.

Normally, for analog analysis of transients, exponential averaging will be used, and it is important to be aware of the special properties of exponential averagers with respect to impulsive inputs. In Ref.3.1 it is shown how the effective averaging time for impulsive inputs is equal to RC, as opposed to $2RC$ for stationary signals. This is illustrated in Fig.3.69 (from Ref.3.1) which shows the response of various averagers to a suddenly applied oscillating transient. It will be noticed that initially the curve for exponential averaging with time $T_A = RC$ follows the curve for linear averaging over time T_A but after a while, on a more stationary part of the signal, the curve for $T_A = 2RC$ gives a better result.

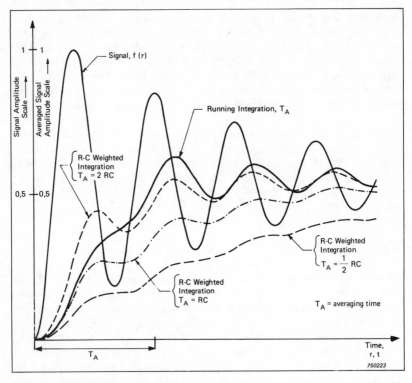

Fig.3.69. Comparison of RC-weighted averaging and running integration of a transient signal

Normally, the indicated averaging time on analog analyzers assumes stationary signals and is based on $T_A = 2RC$ (c.f. Eqn.(3.8)). Thus when applied to impulsive signals it will give a result 3 dB higher than linear averaging with the same nominal averaging time.

This is illustrated in Fig.3.70, which shows the maximum response of both linear and RC-type RMS detectors as a function of the ratio of pulse length to averaging time (Ref.3.9). The curve for linear integration, as would be expected, falls off with 10 dB per decade from an initial value of 0 dB (where the averaging time is equal to the pulse length). For a tone burst of length T_E, for example, the result is indistinguishable from that of a continuous sinewave when $T_A = T_E$, while with $T_A = 10\ T_E$, the same energy is spread over a 10 times longer period and the result (effectively the power) is 10 dB lower. Exponential

146

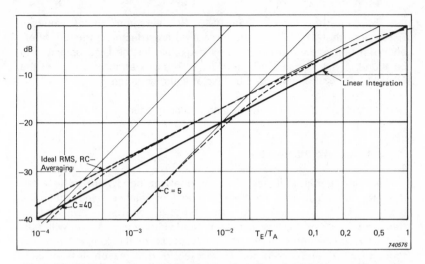

Fig.3.70. Valid range for the factor impulse length: averaging time
(T_E / T_A) for RMS detectors with different crest factors C

averaging with the same nominal averaging times would give 0 dB for the continuous sinewave but −7 dB for the case where $T_A = 10 T_E$ as indicated by the line for "Ideal RMS, RC-averaging". In the range of T_E / T_A between 0,1 and 1 the output of a practical RC-averaging detector changes from "Ideal RMS, RC-averaging" to "Linear integration" as indicated by the dotted line. Thus, at least for detectors with a high crest factor capability, the ratio T_E / T_A should always be less than 0,1.

Fig.3.70 also shows the effect of crest factor for Wahrman detectors. This limits the lower values of the ratio T_E / T_A, as indicated by the asymptotic lines falling off at 20 dB/decade (and corresponding to the "absolute" integration of linear rather than squared values) and the dotted transition lines. For the particular case of crest factor $C = 5$ (which for example applies to the Real-Time Analyzer Type 3347 and the Heterodyne Analyzer Type 2010) it will be seen that the characteristic never reaches the theoretical line for "Ideal RMS, RC-averaging" but on the other hand is approximately parallel with it over the range of T_E / T_A from 0,03 to 0,3. With a small calibration adjustment of 1 dB or so it is thus possible to use these detectors within that range. For detectors with a crest factor capability of 40, the valid range is very wide, with no correction required for T_E / T_A ratios between 0,001 and 0,1.

For the LMS detectors mentioned in Section 3.2.5 it is possible to

147

use the same line as for "Ideal RMS, RC-averaging" for all values of T_E/T_A less than 0,1. The limitation due to crest factor, although different from that shown in Fig.3.70, is negligible for the LMS detectors to be found in B & K measuring amplifiers. The limitation on range of the factor T_E/T_A will be governed by loss of dynamic range.

The various analysis parameters should be chosen as follows:

3.7.3.1. Analyzer Bandwidth

There is very little direct effect of analyzer bandwidth, which can thus be either constant absolute or constant relative bandwidth. The method is in fact valid for the type of analysis discussed in Section 3.7.2 i.e. narrow constant bandwidth analysis but will normally require a longer analysis time (because of the longer averaging times involved) and would not be selected for that reason. It is virtually the only method which can be used, however, for 1/3-octave analysis with the 1/3-octave Real-Time Analyzer Type 3347 or 1/3-octave filter sets. In this case, the filter response time T_R varies with frequency and below a certain frequency will be greater than the pulse length itself. The lower limiting frequency (and thus bandwidth) will therefore be reached when the filter output pulse length falls outside the valid range for the detector (see Section 3.7.3.2).

3.7.3.2. Averaging Time

Use should be made of Fig.3.70 to select a suitable averaging time with respect to the filter output pulse length. For example, as previously mentioned, for a crest factor capability of 5 the averaging time T_A should be chosen such that

$$0,03 \leqslant T_{Eo}/T_A \leqslant 0,3 \tag{3.43}$$

where T_{Eo} is the effective length of the filter output pulse. T_{Eo} will be determined either as the effective length of the original pulse, i.e.

$$T_{Eo} = T_E \tag{3.44}$$

or as the filter response time, i.e.

$$T_{Eo} \approx \frac{1}{B} \tag{3.45}$$

Normally, the greater of the two would govern (in particular when the transient is a time-windowed stationary signal) and the greater should always be used to determine the *minimum* value of averaging time. In some cases, however, where particular frequency components are very localised in the transient (e. g. the steps at each end of a rectangular pulse) then the *maximum* value of averaging time (with respect to crest factor) should be based on (twice) the filter response time. In case of doubt, the crest factor of the filter output signal should be measured.

Calibration of the results is easiest when the averaging time is constant for all frequencies, and for the Real-Time Analyzer Type 3347 this will only apply for the following 3 cases:

1. In the so-called "Sine" Mode the averaging time is constant (200 ms) for all frequencies from 200 Hz and upwards, and in this range the analysis would be valid for T_{E_O} between 6 ms and 60 ms. The frequencies below 200 Hz can also be used, but because of the variable averaging time, a separate calibration must be made in each band.

2. In the "Slow Random" Mode, the averaging time is constant (20 s) for all frequencies and this would thus be valid for pulse lengths between 0,6 and 6 s.

3. Some people have no use for the "Slow Random" Mode and have modified the 3347 to have another constant averaging time in place of "Slow Random". A typical example applies where the analyzer has been modified to allow measurement of aircraft flyover noise according to FAA regulations, where 1,5 — 2 s averaging time is specified. This then also permits analysis of filter output pulses between about 50 and 500 ms in length.

3.7.3.3. Repetition Time

The time between successive playbacks should be such that the detector is able to fall at least 10 dB more than the maximum difference between adjacent frequency estimates. For narrow band analysis, Equation (3.40) will still apply, but in the case of, for example, 1/3-octave measurements, it is quite possible that the bandwidth of the function being measured is considerably less than that of the analyzer and thus it is possible for a situation similar to that illustrated in Fig.3.37 to arise. Hence, a conservative estimate would be given by:

$$T_{rep} \geqslant 5T_A \qquad\qquad (3.46)$$

With the Real-Time Analyzer Type 3347 it is only necessary to play the transient once, using the "Max." facility to store the maximum output level in each channel.

3.7.3.4. Sweep Speed

With a set of fixed filters (e. g. 1/3 octave) it is necessary that the dwell time T_D be equal to the repetition time T_{rep}. Thus, it is necessary either to trigger playback of the transient from the filter shift pulses (e. g. where these are controlled by a Level Recorder) or alternatively to control the filter shift pulses (and paper movement) synchronous with the successive playbacks.

In the case of a sweeping filter analysis it should be ensured that the spacing between spectrum samples is not greater than the bandwidth, and thus Equation (3.41) applies in this case also. Since $T_A >> T_R$ (Eqns. (3.43) and (3.45)) and $T_{rep} >> T_A$ (Eqn.(3.46)) the displacement of the results in frequency will be negligible (Table 3.5).

The sweep speed can then be calculated by dividing the filter bandwidth by T_D as discussed in Sections 3.5.2.5, 3.5.2.7 and 3.5.2.8. Note that AC recording **cannot** be used in this case, as the effective averaging time of the level recorder varies greatly for impulsive inputs.

3.7.3.5. Calibration of Results

Since the energy in the pulse is spread out over a time corresponding to the effective averaging time, then if the averaging were linear, the results in power units (e. g. V^2) or PSD (e. g. V^2/Hz) could be converted into the equivalent energy units (V^2s) or ESD ($V^2 s/Hz$) by multiplying by the averaging time T_A.

For exponential averaging, however, as already discussed, the measured result is 3 dB higher than with linear averaging, and thus the factor with which to multiply is $T_A/2$. This assumes the "Ideal RMS, RC-averaging" characteristic of Fig.3.70, and any deviations from this must be allowed for separately (see example in Section 3.7.4). It is also possible, and probably advisable, to calibrate the system using a known signal such as a rectangular pulse or tone burst.

3.7.4. Examples

To assist in assessing the influence of the various factors which play a role and to compare the pros and cons of the various analysis methods, a transient signal was analyzed in all of the 4 ways illustrated in Fig.3.64.

The signal used was a tone burst of length approx. 10 ms, recorded in a 7502 Digital Event Recorder with 10K memory. The circulation time of the memory (for input sample rate 100 kS/s) was approximately 100 ms. The frequency of the tone was approximately 1 kHz, but in fact adjusted to 976,6 Hz to compensate for the actual pulse length 10,24 ms (and repetition time 102,4 ms) thus ensuring that there were exactly 10 periods in the tone burst. The RMS level of the sinusoidal part was 3,16 V (see Fig.3.71). The analysis setup is shown in Fig.3.72, but it should be noted that the Measuring Amplifier Type 2607 was not always used; in some cases the DC output of the 2010 was taken directly to the Level Recorder Type 2307.

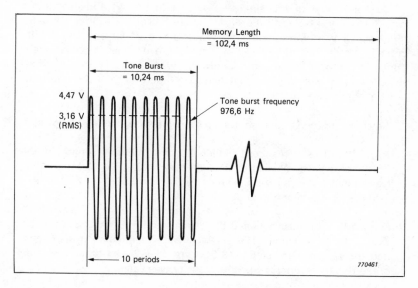

Fig.3.71. Test signal

151

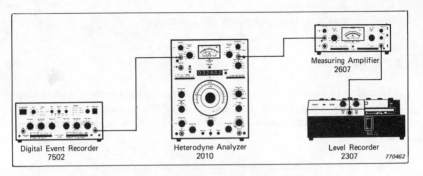

Digital Event Recorder
7502

Heterodyne Analyzer
2010

Level Recorder
2307   770462

Fig.3.72. Instrument set-up for example analyses

The four different analysis methods will now be discussed in some detail.

3.7.4.1. Analysis as a Periodic Signal (c.f. Section 3.7.1)

The tone burst occupied 10% of the memory of the Digital Event Recorder, so that there was a good chance that there would be no problems with crest factor. The total RMS level of the periodic signal was 10 dB below that of the sinusoidal section (i. e. 1 V) and peak value was $3,16\sqrt{2} \approx 4,5$ V, and therefore the crest factor of 4,5 for the unfiltered signal was within the limit of 5 for the 2010 and 2607. The crest factor of the filtered signal would be even less, since as mentioned in the next section, the bandwidth was so chosen that the filter response time was equal to the repetition time and thus the filter output signal almost stationary.

The choice of the various analysis parameters was made as follows:

1. T_{rep} = 100 ms. This corresponded to the memory length of the 7502, and gave a spectral line spacing $(1/T_{rep})$ of 10 Hz, which was suitably narrow with respect to B_{eff} (= $1/T_E$ = 1/0,010 s = 100 Hz) for the tone burst.

2. B = 10 Hz. This just satisfied the requirement of Eqn.(3.31) that $B \geqslant 1/T_{rep}$ (= 1/100 ms = 10 Hz). As already mentioned, it also satisfied the requirement of Eqn.(3.32), viz. $B < B_{eff}$, so that expression of the results as Energy Spectral Density was valid.

3. T_A = 0,3 s. This represented a value of K in Eqn.(3.33) of 3, but

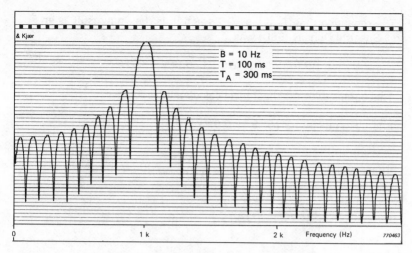

Fig.3.73. Analysis as a periodic signal

was found to be adequate to damp out fluctuations because the filter response time was of the order of the repetition time.

4. T_D = 0,6 s. This was chosen as twice the averaging time (K_A = 2 in Table 3.5) as this is suitable for the 2010).

5. B_{eq} = 0,75 mm. This resulted in a suitable total length for the total analysis ($\approx$ 200 mm) and could be obtained with the 2010 and 2307. The resulting paper speed (Eqn.(3.21)) was thus given by

$$P \leqslant \frac{B_{eq}}{T_D} = \frac{0,75 \ mm}{0,6 \ s} \qquad \therefore \quad \text{Select 1 mm/s}$$

Note that the corresponding value of "Drive Shaft II r. p. m." to give the required value of B_{eq} was 12 rpm (in the Frequency Range "Lin. x1" and with internal gear 10:1 on the 2010).

The resulting analysis is given in Fig.3.73.

6. Scaling — The voltage corresponding to FSD on the recording paper was 0,32 V, corresponding to a power of 0,1 V^2. The analyzer bandwidth was 10 Hz, and therefore the maximum P.S.D. of the result was:

$$\frac{0,1 \ V^2}{10 \ Hz} = 0,01 \ V^2/Hz$$

153

The repetition time T_{rep} was 0,1 s and thus the final result as an Energy Spectral Density (ESD) was:

$$0,01 \ V^2/Hz \cdot 0,1 \ s = 0,001 \ V^2 s/Hz$$

This agrees with the theoretical calculation as follows:

Energy in pulse $= 3,16^2 V^2 \cdot 0,01 \ s = 0,1 \ V^2 s$

Effective bandwidth $\quad B_{eff} = \dfrac{1}{T_E} = \dfrac{1}{0,01s} = 100 \ Hz$

$$\therefore \ ESD = \frac{0,1 \ V^2 s}{100 \ Hz} = 0,001 \ V^2 s/Hz$$

3.7.4.2. Analysis using Peak Detection (c.f. Section 3.7.2)

The various analysis parameters were chosen as follows:

1. $B = 3,16$ Hz. This more than satisfied Eqn.(3.34) which requires $B < 20$ Hz, but it was desired to compare the results with those for short-term RMS averaging (section 3.7.4.3) and this required that the filter response time T_R (320 ms) was somewhat longer than the averaging time (100 ms minimum). Thus, this analysis was considerably less efficient than it could have been. On the other hand, it was possible to allow the detector to fall with a time constant corresponding to $T_A = 0,1$ s rather than triggering the "reset" function, which would have required a more complicated setup.

2. $T_{rep} = 1$ s. This satisfied the requirement of Eqn.(3.38) of $T_{rep} \geqslant 2/B = 2/3,16 = 0,63$ s and, incidentally, at the sweep speed used, gave successive peaks separated by less than the pen thickness, so that the envelope of the peaks was very well demarcated. Since the rate of fall from the peak level was controlled by the set averaging time T_A ($= 0,1$ s) it had to be checked that Eqn.(3.40) was also satisfied, i. e.

$$T_{rep} \geqslant 3 \cdot T_A = 0,3 s \qquad \therefore \ O.K.$$

3. With the narrower bandwidth, $B_{eq} = 0,24$ mm and thus in order to satisfy Eqn.(3.41) the paper speed would have to be less than

154

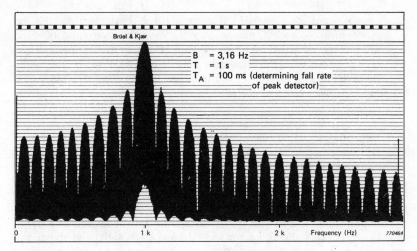

Fig.3.74. Analysis using peak detection

0,24 mm/s. However, in this case it was decided to make the paper speed 0,3 mm/s, resulting in T_D = 0,8 s.

The justification for this was that the analyzer bandwidth was so much smaller than that of the function being measured (3 vs 100 Hz) and the steps between successive peaks (0,3 mm) were less than the line thickness. The resulting analysis is depicted in Fig.3.74.

4. Scaling — The measured peak voltage corresponding to F.S.D. was 0,14 V. Using Eqn.(3.42) and squaring, the corresponding ESD is

$$\frac{V^2_{peak}}{2B^2} = \frac{0,14^2\,V^2}{2 \cdot 3,16^2\,Hz^2} = \frac{0,02\,V^2s}{20\,Hz} = 0,001\ V^2s/Hz$$

as before.

3.7.4.3. Analysis using Short-term RMS Detection (c.f. Section 3.7.2)

1. Analysis parameters were exactly the same as for peak detection as described in Section 3.7.4.2 with the exception that the peak detection was replaced by RMS detection with T_A = 0,1 s. The resulting analysis (with unchanged amplification) is depicted in Fig.3.75.

155

2. Scaling — As discussed in Section 3.7.4.2, because the filter response time T_R (≈ 300 ms) is only 3 times the averaging time T_A (100 ms) the recorded result is 3,5 — 4 dB below that for peak detection compared with the expected 3 dB. If it had not been possible to calibrate the system, the result obtained by adjusting by 3 dB would have been very close to correct.

3.7.4.4. Analysis using Max. RMS Level (c. f. Section 3.7.3)

Parameters were selected as follows:

1. B = 10 Hz. In contrast to the analysis just discussed, it was no longer necessary to have the filter response time longer than the averaging time, and in fact an advantage to have it as short as possible. 10 Hz was the largest standard bandwidth satisfying the condition that it was less than 1/5 the bandwidth of the function itself. It also allows a more direct comparison with the results of Section 3.7.4.1 (Fig.3.73).

2. T_A = 0,3 s. This is at the lower limit of the allowable range indicated in Eqn.(3.43) for a crest factor of 5, but is acceptable in this case where it is known that the effective length T_{Eo} is the same for all fre-

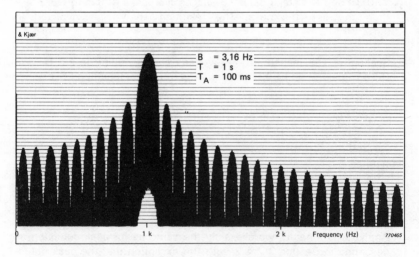

Fig.3.75. Analysis using short-term RMS detection
(Same amplification as Fig.3.72)

quencies (determined in all cases by Eqn.(3.45) because of the constant bandwidth.) In a physically generated transient this is not certain (the high frequencies have a tendency to die out more rapidly) and moreover for constant percentage bandwidth the filter response time varies with frequency, so that it is advisable to choose the ratio T_E/T_A closer to 0,1.

3. T_{rep} = 1 s. Because of the relatively narrow bandwidth it was sufficient to satisfy Eqn.(3.40), i. e. $T_{rep} \geqslant 3T_A$.

4. Taking T_D = 1 s to satisfy Eqn.(3.41) the maximum sweep speed is given by B_{eq}/T_D = 0,75 mm/s and thus 0,3 mm/s was again selected.

The resulting analysis is shown in Fig.3.76. The amplification was exactly the same as for the analysis of Section 3.7.4.1 (Fig.3.73).

5. Scaling — In comparison with the analysis of Fig.3.73, for which the bandwidth was the same, the difference in scaling would arise from the fact that the measured PSD units should here be multiplied by $T_A/2$ (i. e. 150 ms) whereas in that case the multiplying factor was the repetition time T_{rep} (100 ms). From this, it would be expected that the results should be $10 \log_{10} (1,5)$ = 2 dB below those

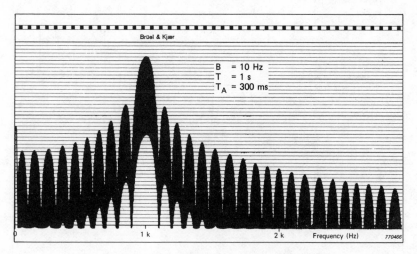

Fig.3.76. Analysis using max. RMS Level
(Same amplification as Fig.3.71)

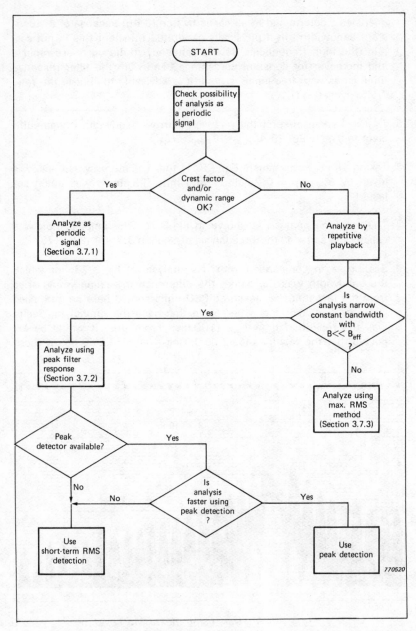

START

Check possibility
of analysis as
a periodic
signal

Crest factor
and/or
dynamic range
OK?

Yes

No

Analyze as
periodic
signal
(Section 3.7.1)

Analyze by
repetitive
playback

Is
analysis narrow
constant bandwidth
with
$B \ll B_{eff}$
?

Yes

No

Analyze using
peak filter
response
(Section 3.7.2)

Analyze using
max. RMS
method
(Section 3.7.3)

Peak
detector available?

Yes

No

Is
analysis
faster using
peak detection
?

No

Yes

Use
short-term RMS
detection

Use
peak detection

770520

Fig.3.77. Flow diagram for selection of analysis method

158

of Fig.3.73, instead of the actual 4 dB. The major part of the difference can be explained by reference to Fig.3.70, where for T_E / T_A = 0,3 (as applies here) the actual detector characteristic is approx. 1,5 dB below the theoretical line for "Ideal RMS, RC-averaging". It should be remembered that in a practical case the ratio T_{Eo} / T_A should have been chosen smaller, but it was difficult to find an example on which all 4 methods could be used, keeping in mind that they are best adapted to different situations.

3.7.5. Summary

The foregoing information on the selection of the best analysis method in a given case has been summarized in a flow diagram, reproduced here as Fig.3.77.

4. DIGITAL FILTERING

It is not the intention here to go into details of digital filter design (see for example Refs. (4.1), (4.2)), just to explain what digital filtering is, and in particular in what ways it differs from the other major digital analysis technique, viz. FFT (see Chapter 5). Its use for practical measurements will also be discussed. The term "digital filter" is here used to mean a digital processor which receives a sequence of input data values, carries out some digital operation on them and outputs a corresponding sequence of digital values which are filtered in some way with respect to the input (Fig.4.1). In fact the term will be limited to so-called "recursive digital filtering". In contrast to FFT, which operates on whole blocks of data at a time, recursive digital filtering is a continuous process and for every input data value an output data value is obtained. In this way, digital filtering is similar to analog filtering, and in fact it is possible to design digital filters with properties similar to those of virtually any practical filter. It is even possible to design digital filters which are not physically realizable in analog form, but these generally have undesirable properties and will not be considered here.

As an introduction to digital filtering, the example will be taken of a simple lowpass filter of the RC type such as is widely used for "expon-

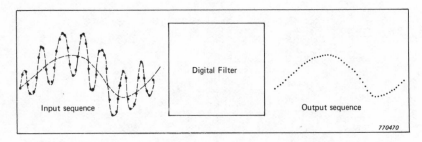

Fig.4.1. Input to and output from a digital filter

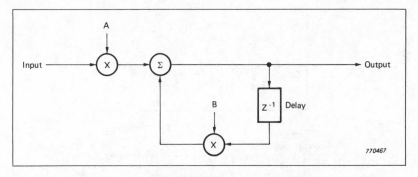

Fig.4.2. Schematic diagram for a single-pole filter

ential averaging". This is the case which was discussed in connection with Time Compression Analysis at the end of Section 3.5.4.2. Fig.4.2 is a schematic diagram of such an averager, illustrating how it can be made up of standard digital components, e. g. adders, multipliers, a delay unit and a read-only memory (ROM) for storing the constants A and B.

For each sample period, the new data sample entering the filter is multiplied by the constant A and added to B times the previous output value which has been stored in a delay unit. For the example illustrated in Fig.3.54 the constant A was 0,1 while the constant B was 0,9. In fact, in order not to change the amplification the sum of A and B must be 1, so that in reality there is only one independent parameter with which the properties of the filter can be varied. As remarked in Section 3.5.4.2 this single parameter can be related to the equivalent averaging time. Note that the averaging time is defined only in relation to the sampling period, which is the same as saying that the lowpass filter cut-off frequency is only defined in relation to the sampling frequency (the reciprocal of the sampling period).

Fig.4.3 illustrates the effect of carrying out the operations of Fig.4.2 on a sampled squared sinusoidal signal. The input signal, varying between 0 and 1, could be considered to be the output from a squaring circuit of a sinusoidal signal of amplitude 1. It has somewhat fortuitously been sampled (4 times per period) at the values 0, 0,5, 1,0 and 0,5 but since this obeys Shannon's Sampling Theorem (see p.19) no error will be introduced. It can for example be checked that the RMS level of the samples over one period is the same as that of the continuous sinusoid. Thus, the first sample (0,5) is multiplied by 0,1 and added to 90% of zero, giving 0,05. The next sample (1,0) is also multiplied by

161

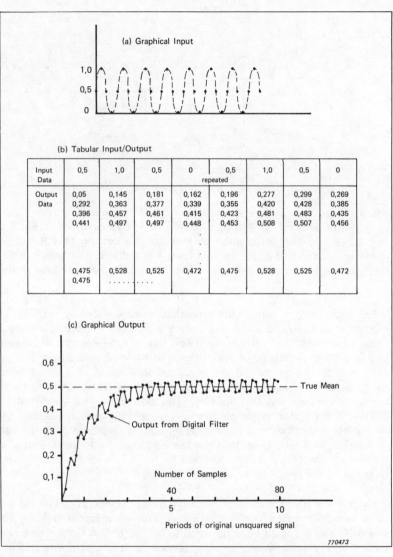

(a) Graphical Input

(b) Tabular Input/Output

Input Data	0,5	1,0	0,5	0 repeated	0,5	1,0	0,5	0
Output Data	0,05	0,145	0,181	0,162	0,196	0,277	0,299	0,269
	0,292	0,363	0,377	0,339	0,355	0,420	0,428	0,385
	0,396	0,457	0,461	0,415	0,423	0,481	0,483	0,435
	0,441	0,497	0,497	0,448	0,453	0,508	0,507	0,456
				.				
				.				
				.				
	0,475	0,528	0,525	0,472	0,475	0,528	0,525	0,472
	0,475	. . . .						

(c) Graphical Output

True Mean

Output from Digital Filter

Number of Samples

Periods of original unsquared signal

770473

Fig.4.3. Effect of filter from Fig.4.2 for A = 0,1 and B = 0,9

0,1 and added to 90% of 0,05 giving 0,145 and so on. It is seen that there is first a period in which the filter output rises, but that finally the output value levels out though with a small fluctuation (see Fig.4.3). The correct average is of course 0,5, but the output fluctuates about this with a ripple sampled at the four values 0,472, 0,475, 0,525 and 0,528. These samples no longer correspond to the peaks as with the original signal (because of a phase shift) but it can be calculated that the amplitude of the fluctuation is 0,0375 corresponding to ± 0,3 dB. This agrees well with the result obtained from Fig.3.15 for the equivalent analog detector. It will be remembered from Fig.3.54 that the RC-time constant in this case was approx. 10 sample periods, giving an equivalent averaging time of 20 sample periods. The squared sinusoid was sampled 4 times per period corresponding to 8 times per period for the original unsquared signal. Thus the averaging time corresponds to 2,5 periods of the original signal, and it is this which gives 0,3 dB ripple when inserted in Fig.3.15.

4.1. THE Z-TRANSFORM

Although it is not intended to go into details, it may be useful to explain some points of terminology which are often heard in connection with digital filters. One of these is the so-called z-transform.

The z-transform is defined (Ref.4.1) as:

$$G(z) = \sum_{n=-\infty}^{\infty} g(n\,\Delta t) z^{-n} \qquad (4.1)$$

where z is a complex variable.

By making the substitution $z = e^{j2\pi f \Delta t}$ (a circle of radius 1) it will be seen that Eqn.(4.1) reduces to that form of the Fourier transform which applies to sampled time functions, viz. Eqn.(2.16), and the latter can thus be considered as the z-transform evaluated on the unit circle (i.e. $|z| = 1$). Note that on the unit circle, the sampling frequency f_s (= $1/\Delta t$) gives $z = e^{j2\pi} = 1$, as do all multiples of it, which is another expression of the periodicity of the frequency spectrum alluded to in Fig.2.6 part 3. Fig.4.4 illustrates this, and shows for example how the Nyquist frequency f_N is located at $z = -1$; the angles from 0 to π represent the frequencies 0 to f_N, while the angles from $-\pi$ (= π) around to 0 represent the frequencies from f_N to f_s, or equally, the negative frequencies from $-f_N$ to zero, because of the periodicity.

The z-transform bears the same kind of relationship to the discrete-time Fourier transform (Eqn.(2.16)) as the Laplace transform does to the Fourier Integral Transform (Eqn.(2.14)), but applies to discrete time

163

sequences rather than continuous functions. In particular, it has very similar properties with respect to difference equations as the Laplace transform does with respect to differential equations, in general reducing the solution of an Nth-order equation to finding the roots of an Nth-order polynomial in the transform domain (Ref.4.1).

Those familiar with Laplace transform methods will remember that a filter whose function is described by an Nth-order differential equation in general has N poles in the Laplace domain, each one corresponding to the root of an Nth-order polynomial which forms the denominator of the Laplace transform of the impulse response (i. e. the transfer function). The same applies to the z-transform for the case of an Nth-order difference equation (which may be an approximation to the differential equation or a system characteristic in its own right).

It is of interest to see how a delay corresponds to an integration, and the simplest example of this is provided by the RC-lowpass filter already discussed. The differential equation applicable to its characteristic is:

$$\frac{dh(t)}{dt} = -\frac{h(t)}{RC} \tag{4.2}$$

which says that the rate of *fall* of the capacitor voltage is proportional to the voltage and inversely proportional to the RC time constant. As already given in Eqn.(3.7) the solution to this equation is:

$$h(t) = e^{-t/RC} \tag{4.3}$$

for unit input.

The simple (backward) difference equation corresponding to Eqn.(4.2) may be derived as:

$$\frac{\Delta h}{\Delta t} = -\frac{h}{RC}$$

or

$$\frac{h(n) - h(n-1)}{\Delta t} = -\frac{h(n-1)}{RC}$$

giving

$$h(n) = h(n-1)\left[1 - \frac{\Delta t}{RC}\right] \tag{4.4}$$

164

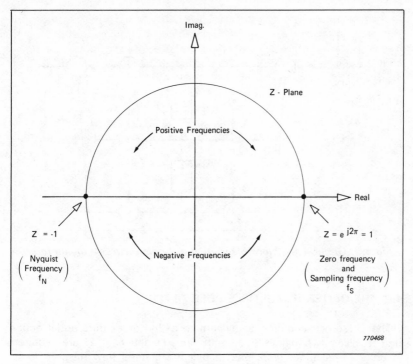

Fig.4.4. Frequencies in the z-plane
(conventional representation with real axis horizontal)

This shows how the value of $h(n)$ (i. e. the integration of dh/dt) can be obtained from the previous value $h(n-1)$ making use of the constant $\Delta t/RC$. Thus a single integration involves one delay.

As a matter of interest, by repeated application of Eqn.(4.4) it will be seen that $h(n)$ reduces to:

$$h(n) = h(o)\left[1 - \frac{\Delta t}{RC}\right]^n \tag{4.5}$$

and this may be checked with the successive values of Fig.3.54 where both $h(o)$ and $\Delta t/RC$ were equal to 0,1.

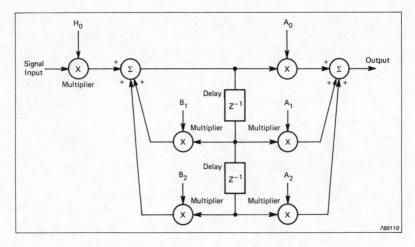

Fig.4.5. Generalised block diagram of a 2-pole recursive digital filter

4.2. THE GENERAL MULTIPLE-POLE FILTER

The difference equation equivalent to a 2nd order differential equation involves two delays (i.e. both $h(n-1)$ and $h(n-2)$ are required in order to calculate $h(n)$), and in fact the general flow diagram for a 2nd order system (2-pole filter) is as illustrated in Fig.4.5.

It is possible to generate digital equivalents of all the well-known filter types e.g. Butterworth, Chebyshev, etc. (Ref.4.2). Because of the periodicity of the frequency function, they can never be exactly the same, but by careful design the differences can be made negligible. Multiple-pole filters (generally required to achieve steep filter flanks) can be formed by cascading 2-pole sections, with appropriate choice of coefficients.

One of the main advantages of a digital filter is that the same hardware can be used to generate virtually any filter shape (with the same number of poles) just by changing the filter coefficients used in the calculations. For example, it is possible to change the same calculating unit from a bandpass to a lowpass filter, or to change the centre frequency or bandwidth just by changing the filter coefficients. Once decided, the filter coefficients completely determine the filter properties, and for example these do not change with time; the filter never needs trimming.

166

Digital filters are best adapted to logarithmic frequency scales and constant percentage bandwidth, in contrast to FFT which intrinsically gives constant bandwidth on a linear frequency scale.

To illustrate these points, the design of the B & K Real-Time 1/3-octave Analyzer Type 2131 will be considered.

4.3. THE B & K DIGITAL FREQUENCY ANALYZER TYPE 2131

The Digital Frequency Analyzer Type 2131 is depicted in Fig.4.6. Although considerably more compact than the analog analyzer it replaced (the B & K Type 3347, see Fig.3.30), it has basically the same function, viz. producing averaged 1/3-octave spectra in real-time in the frequency range up to 20 kHz. Its major advantages, however, are that it has a larger dynamic range (display range 60 dB instead of 50 dB), lower limiting frequency 1,6 Hz as standard (instead of 20 Hz), a choice between octave and 1/3-octave bandwidth, a choice between linear and exponential averaging (instead of exponential only) and a choice between a range of constant averaging times and constant BT_A products giving constant statistical confidence (standard deviation of the error

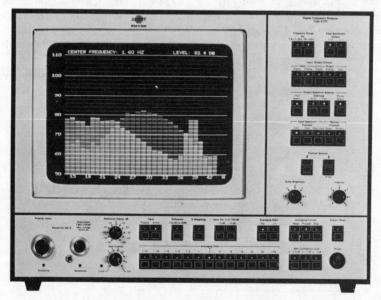

Fig.4.6. The B & K Digital Frequency Analyzer Type 2131

< 0,5, 1 or 2 dB). There are other advantages, but the above are those which derive from its construction as a digital filter, and it is that which is of interest here. The way in which the advantages arise will become obvious from a consideration of its mode of operation.

Before looking at the overall construction of the analyzer, it is of interest to consider the design of the individual filter units. In place of the general 2-pole diagram of Fig.4.5, they have a special schematic diagram as illustrated in Fig.4.7. This has the obvious advantage that fewer adders and multipliers are required, while by making use of the so-called "matched z-transform" it is still possible to design equivalents of the well-known bandpass and lowpass filter types. It will be appreciated that the three coefficients remaining provide the required flexibility to determine both the resonant frequency and Q-factor for a damped resonator, and to vary the overall amplification.

Fig.4.8 is a block diagram of the input and filter section of the 2131. It will be seen that the signal, shortly after entry, is converted into digital form and from then on all operations are digital. Before analog-to-digital (A/D) conversion, the signal is first lowpass filtered with a 12-pole analog lowpass filter having its cut-off at 27 kHz which is above the highest frequency of interest, viz. 22,4 kHz (the upper limiting frequency of the 1/3-octave centred on 20 kHz). This is done to avoid aliasing (section 2.2.4). The A/D converter used gives 12-bit resolution, and this in combination with 15-bit calculations and 9-bit filter coeffi-

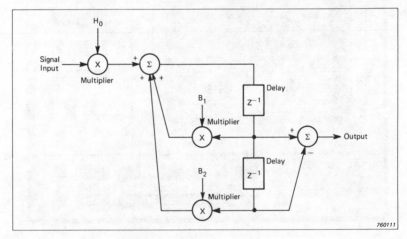

Fig.4.7. Block diagram of 2-pole digital filter used in the 2131

168

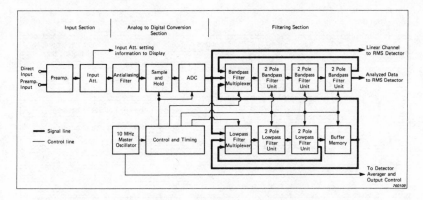

Fig.4.8. Block diagram of input and filter section of 2131

cients, gives a resulting spectrum with more than 69 dB dynamic range. The sample rate of the A/D converter is 66,667 kHz.

Each sample coming from the A/D converter is passed simultaneously through a 1/3-octave bandpass filtering section and a lowpass filtering section. In fact, each sample is passed through each section three times for the following reasons:

(1) **1/3-octave filtering** The 1/3-octave filter section consists of three 2-pole filter units in series and for each pass, coefficients are used which give a 6-pole Chebyshev filter of 1/3-octave bandwidth. For each pass, the filter coefficients are changed so as to obtain successively the three 1/3-octave centre frequencies in each octave (e. g. 20 kHz, 16 kHz and 12,5 kHz in the highest octave). These three filter characteristics are illustrated in Fig.4.9.

(2) **Low-pass filtering** The low-pass filter section consists of two 2-pole filter units in series. Thus, during the three passes used to obtain the three 1/3-octave filtered values, it is possible to circulate the data value three times through the lowpass filter section, achieving 12-pole lowpass filtration (in this case, incidentally, a Butterworth filter was used). The cut-off frequency of the lowpass filter is one octave lower than the previous maximum frequency content.

The reason for the lowpass filtration is that it makes it possible to discard every second sample without losing any further information, i. e. once the highest octave in frequency is filtered away it is quite valid to

169

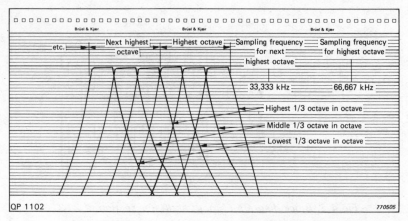

Fig.4.9. Filter characteristic vs. sampling frequency

use half the previous sample rate while still complying with Shannon's sampling theorem (see footnote p. 19). These lowpass filtered samples with half the sampling frequency can now be fed back to the bandpass filter section, and since the filter characteristics are defined only in relation to the sampling frequency, the same filter coefficients will now give the three 1/3-octave filters one octave lower in frequency (see Fig.4.9).

In a similar manner, the same filtered samples can be fed back to the lowpass filter section and again filtered to one octave lower, once again allowing each second sample to be discarded, and so on.

It is possible to continue in this way for all lower octaves, thus obtaining the complete 1/3-octave spectrum. This explains the presence of the multiplexers at entry to both filter sections. These must keep track of where the next sample to be filtered is located and where the result is to be placed. It will be found that provided it is possible to process a sample from the A/D converter (i. e. in the highest frequency octave) plus one other sample in each sample period, it is possible to produce a parallel real-time spectrum for all octaves up to and including the highest. The limitation at the low frequency end is not in calculating capacity, only in being able to store the results, and so in the 2131 the frequency range is limited to a little over 4 decades. The reason why this is possible can be understood by reference to Fig.4.10. This is a table showing the order of processing, at least of the first few samples in each octave, both in the 1/3-octave section and in the lowpass filter section. The lowpass filtered values (with every second one discarded)

170

BANDPASS FILTER

SAMPLING PERIOD NUMBER

B.P. Filter Octave	1	2	3	4	5	6	7	8	9	10	11	12	13	14	15	16
16 kHz	1	2	3	4	5	6	7	8	9	10	11	12	13	14	15	16
8 kHz	1_1		3_1		5_1		7_1		9_1		11_1		13_1		15_1	
4 kHz		1_2				5_2				9_2				13_2		
2 kHz				1_3								9_3				
1 kHz								1_4								
500 Hz																1_5

LOWPASS FILTER

L.P. Filter Cut-Off Freq.	1	2	3	4	5	6	7	8	9	10	11	12	13	14	15	16
12 kHz	1_1	2_1	3_1	4_1	5_1	6_1	7_1	8_1	9_1	10_1	11_1	12_1	13_1	14_1	15_1	16_1
6 kHz	1_2		3_2		5_2		7_2		9_2		11_2		13_2		15_2	
3 kHz		1_3				5_3				9_3				13_3		
1,5 kHz				1_4								9_4				
750 Hz								1_5								
375 Hz																1_6

Fig.4.10. Operation of 2131 digital filter unit

are fed back to the next lower octave in both filter sections. Considering the number of samples to be processed in each octave, and calling the number in the 16 kHz octave M, the number in the 8 kHz octave is $M/2$, in the 4 kHz octave $M/4$, and so on. Thus the total number of samples to be processed in all octaves below the highest is $M(1/2 + 1/4 + 1/8 + \ldots\ldots\ldots) = M$, i. e. the same as the number of samples in the highest octave alone. Consequently, as shown in Fig.4.10, it is only necessary to process one data value from the highest octave plus one other in each sample period.

This ability to timeshare efficiently when the frequency scale is based on octaves is the major reason why digital filters are so well adapted to logarithmic frequency scales and constant percentage bandwidth. Another results from the fact that the filter characteristics are relative to the sampling frequency and thus tend to be symmetrical and uniform on a logarithmic frequency scale, a desirable property in constant percentage bandwidth filters. This question of filter characteristic is discussed in some detail in section 4.4 since it represents one of the major differences from spectra generated originally by FFT techniques and then converted to constant percentage bandwidth.

The operation of the analyzer can be converted to octave band filter-

171

ing, once again basically by changing the filter coefficients. Since only one filter is to be calculated in each octave it is possible to recirculate the data values more than once through the bandpass filtering section. In the 2131, two passes are used (3 would have been possible) giving 12-pole filters of the Chebyshev type.

So far, only the actual filtering process has been considered, but it is important to consider the averaging as well, since many of the advantages of digital filters over competitive analyzers stem from the correct use of digital averaging (correct in the sense that the sampling theorem is obeyed, and thus no information is lost).

Linear averaging is achieved simply by adding together the squares of the filter output samples● divided by the total number to be averaged. This number is of course equal to the averaging time multiplied by the sample rate for the octave in question. The averaged result is held and is logarithmically converted into dB before display.

Exponential averaging is achieved in a similar way as for time compression analysis (see Section 3.5.4.2 and as discussed in the early part of this section). The equivalent averaging time is based on the Eqn.(3.8) (i. e. $T_A = 2RC$) and thus applies directly to stationary signals. As for linear averaging it is the squared values of the filter output samples which are averaged, and the results are converted to dB before display.

Averaging with **constant standard error**, which is available with exponential averaging only, is achieved by making the averaging time in each octave inversely proportional to the frequency so that a constant BT_A product is obtained for all frequencies (at least for the lowest 1/3-octave filter in each octave; the two higher filters have the same averaging time and thus somewhat higher BT_A product). Since for constant percentage bandwidth a constant BT_A product corresponds to a given number of periods (c. f. Eqn.(3.2)) in this case it will correspond to a given number of samples (for constant sampling ratio i. e. ratio of sampling frequency to filter centre frequency), and thus the *number of samples* averaged will be the same in all octaves. Three values of BT_A product are selectable giving standard error $\epsilon < 0,5$, 1 or 2 dB as desired (c. f. Eqn.(3.9)).

● Squared values are represented by 24 bits and sufficient bits are used in the calculations to avoid overflow

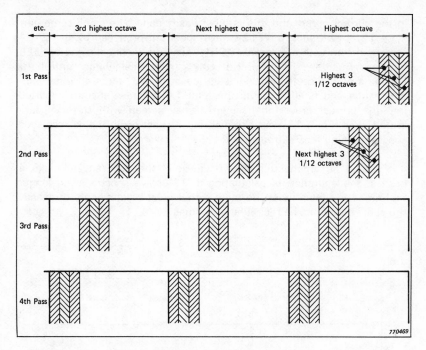

Fig.4.11. Procedure for obtaining 1/12-octave spectrum in 4 passes

4.3.1. 1/12-Octave Analysis

As an example of the flexibility of a digital filter such as the B & K Type 2131, the case of its use for 1/12-octave filtering will be discussed.

As mentioned previously, the filter characteristic obtained from a digital filter is determined entirely by the filter coefficients used in the calculations. These can be chosen to give 1/12-octave bandwidth, and in fact in the 2131 these extra coefficients are programmed as standard in the ROMs used for storing the coefficients (the storage space would otherwise have been unused). However, since there is only calculation and storage capacity to calculate on three filters per octave at any one time, it is necessary to perform four separate analyses, each time accessing three sets of filter coefficients corresponding to three of the 1/12-octave passbands in each octave (see Fig.4.11). As will be evident from Fig.4.11, the results from the 4 passes must be interleaved in the correct order, and this is most easily done by a small computer. Fig.4.12 shows such a 1/12-octave spectrum produced by the 2131 in conjunction with a Tektronix 4051 Calculator (connected via an IEEE Interface Bus, see Ref.4.3). Not only can the calculator control the changing of the coefficients for each pass, it also stores all intermediate results and finally outputs the total 1/12-octave spectrum (sorted into the correct order) on its own display screen with correctly calibrated axes: Fig.4.12 was obtained as a direct copy of this displayed spectrum using the Tektronix Hard Copy Unit No. 4631.

It should be emphasized that because of the necessity to make 4 passes, the operation of calculating 1/12-octave spectra is no longer real-time, and thus either the input signal must be stationary or exactly the same data must be recirculated 4 times.

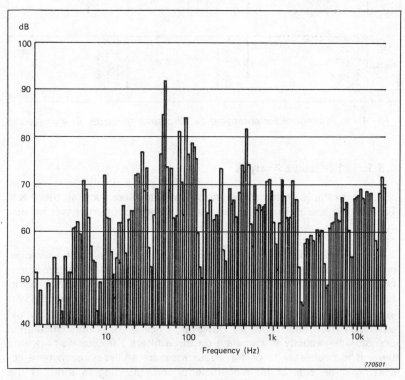

Fig.4.12. 1/12-octave spectrum produced by 2131 in conjunction with a Tektronix 4051 calculator

174

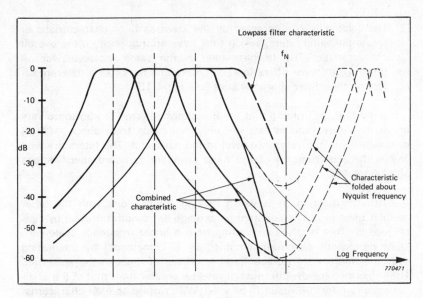

Fig.4.13. Overall filter characteristics including lowpass filtration

4.4. FILTER CHARACTERISTICS

In general, digital filters are designed to resemble one of the well-known classes of analog filters, e.g. Butterworth, Chebyshev, etc., but as mentioned previously there will always be some slight deviation for the following reasons:

(1) Because of the periodicity of the frequency characteristic, there is some overlapping around the Nyquist frequency (aliasing) as illustrated in Fig.4.13. There is also a slight distortion of the characteristic (when the matched z-transform is used) but by careful design this can be made negligible. The overlapping around the Nyquist frequency can obviously be reduced by increasing the "sampling ratio" and for example in the 2131, it is only the highest 1/3-octave filter in each octave which is noticeably affected by folding. On the other hand, increasing the sampling ratio is undesirable since it gives a proportionate reduction in the real-time frequency capability and moreover if carried too far gives rise to stability problems. With the 2131, the sampling ratio varies from 3,3 for the highest 1/3-octave in each octave to 5,3 for the lowest.

175

(2) The folding is counteracted by the lowpass filter characteristic of the antialiasing filters, which thus have an influence on the overall characteristic. The lowpass filter is the same, however, for all three 1/3-octave filters in each octave and thus has a different effect on their filter characteristics (see Fig.4.13).

It must be kept in mind that the deviations referred to above are very minor in nature, and in fact are only detectable from about −30 dB with respect to the reference level in the passband. The filters are well within the requirements of the most stringent standard specifications (e. g. Fig.4.16).

In this connection, it is worth making comparisons with the other method used to obtain constant percentage bandwidth filtration by digital means. This involves converting from a linear frequency scale constant bandwidth spectrum (obtained by FFT methods) by integrating over the appropriate number (and fractions) of lines in the spectrum. The integrated bandwidth must always be greater than that of the original spectrum for the result to be valid. With respect to filter characteristic, it will be seen from Fig.4.14 that because the original filter characteristic is symmetrical on a linear scale, the integrated characteristic will be as well, and thus will be unsymmetrical on a logarithmic frequency scale. Moreover, over one decade the relative steepness of the flanks of filters obtained in this way (i. e. effectively the shape factor) will vary by a factor of 10:1. It is quite common to convert one decade

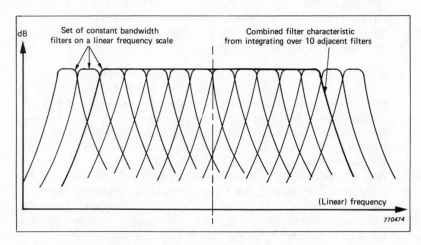

Fig.4.14. Effect on filter characteristic of combining filters

176

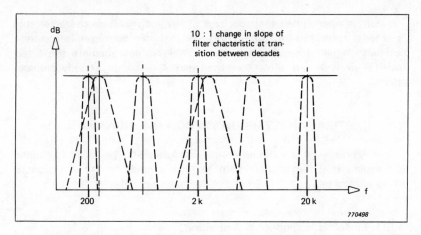

Fig.4.15. Variations in filter characteristic with synthesized constant percentage bandwidth filters

at a time, and thus where two successive decades are fitted together there will be a sudden change of 10:1 in filter flank steepness (see Fig.4.15) even though both might be within the tolerances specified for a particular filter class (see for example Fig.4.16) which in reality are often quite wide.

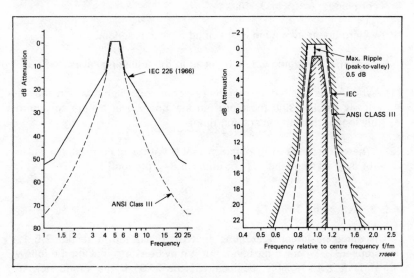

Fig.4.16. 1/3-Octave filter specifications over 20 dB and 80 dB ranges

It will be appreciated that this sort of variation in filter characteristic is at least an order of magnitude greater than that discussed in connection with digital filters, and is undesirable in cases where the filter flanks can have an effect on the results, e. g. for steeply sloping spectra.

4.5. PRACTICAL ANALYSIS OF STATIONARY SIGNALS

The operation of the Digital Frequency Analyzer Type 2131 is almost self-explanatory, but it may help to give a guide to the selection of those parameters which are not decided automatically.

4.5.1. Linear vs. Exponential Averaging

Normally, linear averaging would be chosen in the following cases:

(1) Where the signal sample is limited in length, e. g. a short tape recording.

(2) Where it is desired to minimize the statistical error in a measurement made on a stationary random signal with a certain fixed record length (c. f. Fig.3.35).

(3) Where linear averaging is specified or recommended.

Exponential averaging would be used in the following cases:

(1) Where it is desired to monitor a continuous signal which may be slowly varying (and therefore not stationary over a time considerably longer than the averaging time).

(2) Where it is desired to obtain a result with a uniform statistical error over all frequencies (i. e. uniform BT_A product).

4.5.2. Averaging Time T_A

The same basic considerations apply as discussed in section 3.5.1.1 for stepped 1/3-octave filtration, but it may be worth making the following remarks which apply specifically to the 2131 Digital Frequency Analyzer.

For continuous **deterministic** signals the easiest way to ensure that the averaging time complies with Eqn.(3.15) $(T_A \geqslant 3/f)$ is to check visually that the fluctuations are acceptable, in particular in cases where f is to be interpreted as a beat or modulating frequency smaller than the analyzer bandwidth. It is quite likely that such modulating frequencies will be common to all frequency ranges and thus a constant averaging time will be optimal.

For **stationary random** signals it may be preferred to choose the averaging mode giving constant BT_A product and thus uniform error at all frequencies. One advantage of this is that the result is then known to be valid at all frequencies.

Where it is desired to get maximum information from a **limited record length**, of either a random or deterministic signal, then the averaging time is virtually decided by the record length.Note that the result may not then be valid at all frequencies, since for short averaging times, at least, the BT_A product may be too low.

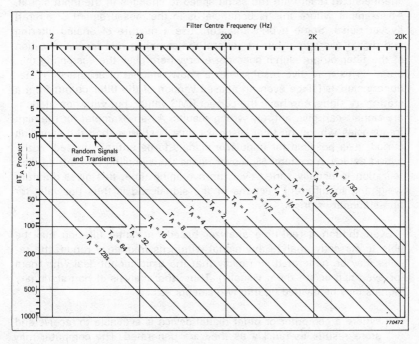

Fig.4.17. BT_A product vs. averaging time T_A for the 2131

Fig.4.17 indicates the BT_A product achieved with the various averaging times over the frequency range of the analyzer. The invalid range where BT_A is less than 1 is not included and a dotted line demarcates the values of BT_A less than 10 for which the result would not normally be valid for random signals. The values of BT_A product may be inserted in Eqn.(3.9) ($\epsilon = 1/(2\sqrt{BT_A})$) or Table 3.4 to obtain the relative standard deviation of the error for gaussian random signals.

4.6. PRACTICAL ANALYSIS OF CONTINUOUS NON-STATIONARY SIGNALS

It is in the analysis of non-stationary signals, both continuous and transient, that the 1/3-octave real-time analyzer based on digital filtering has marked advantages over other types of 1/3-octave real-time analyzers. In comparison with an analog analyzer with analog detectors (e. g. the B & K Type 3347) it has the advantage that it is possible to choose a wide range of constant averaging times, so that all frequency channels can react with the same speed to changes in the input signal. An example where this is beneficial is in the measurement of aircraft flyover noise. Some hybrid analyzers use a mixture of analog filtering and digital averaging, but in general the sampling rate for digitalization of the filter output signal does not everywhere obey the "sampling theorem". This may give results with a known degree of accuracy for stationary signals (since even an aliased version of the filter output from a **stationary** signal can have the correct RMS value), but with non-stationary signals can give entirely wrong results. As an example, for the high frequencies where the filter response time is shorter than the sampling period, it is possible for impulsive signals to be entirely missed by the hybrid detection system. Moreover, since the sampling rate during digitalization is usually varied over the averaging time, this gives different weighting to different sections of the signal and is thus not valid for non-stationary signals.

Even though a real-time analyzer based on digital filtering may be able to correctly analyze any signal within its frequency range, the results may be generated so rapidly that the user cannot deal with them (or even appreciate them visually). Thus, the analysis of non-stationary signals may be divided up into two categories:

(1) Where a computer or other digital device is available to receive and store results as quickly as they are generated. The computer may also be used to control the operation of the analyzer.

180

(2) Where a computer is not available, it is possible to use a time windowing device such as a Gauss Impulse Multiplier to select out a particular portion of a signal which can be repeated (e. g. each cycle of a reciprocating machine can be divided up into short sections by the time window, using various delay times each of which can be held until the results have been obtained in hard copy form). Each windowed sample may then be analyzed as a separate transient, or alternatively it may be desired to make an average over several repetitions.

Each case will be looked at separately.

4.6.1. Analysis with Output to a Computer

With non-stationary signals it is usually best to choose a constant averaging time (rather than constant BT_A product) the averaging time being chosen with respect to how rapidly the signal is changing. The major question to be decided is whether linear or exponential averaging is to be used.

Exponential averaging will generally be easier to use because it gives a continuously updated result, and there is no need to synchronize the digital acquisition of spectra with the averaging time. The time between acquisitions should normally be chosen to be between 0,5 and 1,0 times the averaging time. In certain cases the acquisition time could be made greater than the averaging time. As an example, the case is mentioned of measurement of reverberation time (Ref.4.4) where it is possible to read a spectrum into the computer every 44 ms, and where in this case the averaging time could thus be chosen as short as 1/32 s. The minimum reverberation time which can be measured by this means is thus limited by the maximum rate of fall of the exponential averaging (8,7 dB/averaging time) and would thus be of the order of 10 averaging times or 0,3 s minimum.

The limitation given by the rate of fall of an exponential averager can mean that it is preferable to use linear averaging, using the computer to trigger each averaging cycle and read in the spectra so obtained at intervals corresponding to the averaging time. As an example can be mentioned the case of aircraft flyover noise according to the new IEC recommendations● where the alternative is given of linear averaging with a

---

● IEC Standard, Publication 561, 1st. Ed. 1976

1,5 s averaging time, although sample spectra should be obtained every 0,5 s. With the advent of supersonic civil aircraft, there is an increased likelihood that PNdB calculations based on exponential averaging will be artificially high because the actual aircraft noise falls at a rate greater than 8,7 dB/averaging time and this problem may be eliminated by using linear averaging.

In order to comply with the above-mentioned recommendations, the computer would have to stop the averaging 22 ms before the end of each 0,5 s period to allow digital readout to the computer. An appropriate scaling adjustment could be made in the computer at the same time as three 0,5 s spectra were added together to give 1,5 s averaging time.

4.6.2. Analysis using a Time Window

In this case the discussion of Section 3.6 applies directly (as for the 3347 with constant averaging time). Where the windowed section repeats exactly every time (e. g. a recording on a Digital Event Recorder) it may be preferred to treat the analysis as that of a single transient, using the "max. RMS" method of Section 3.7.3, or linear averaging (Section 4.7) in order to obtain the maximum dynamic range. Where it is desired to make an average over several repetitions of a slightly varying windowed section (e. g. successive firing cycles in a diesel engine) then dynamic range would have to be sacrificed for amplitude stability. The total effective averaging time would be equal to the number of cycles averaged multiplied by the effective window length T_E (Eqn.3.27).

4.7. PRACTICAL ANALYSIS OF TRANSIENTS

Three methods may be used for the analysis of transients:

1) Analysis as a periodic signal.
2) Analysis by the max. RMS method.
3) Linear integration over the transient.

These will each be discussed in turn.

4.7.1. Analysis as a Periodic Signal

Here, the discussion of Section 3.7.1 applies fully. However, with the

2131 this method is not so attractive as with normal analog analysis for the following reasons:

1) It requires that the signal be recorded on a loop (tape loop or Digital Event Recorder) whereas this can be avoided with the other two methods (thus utilizing the real-time capacilities of the analyzer).

2) Dynamic range is restricted in comparison with the other two methods while the result is no more accurate than that using linear integration.

4.7.2. Analysis by the Max. RMS Method (Exponential Averaging)

Here, the discussion of Section 3.7.3 applies, with the following remarks:

1) Because of the true squaring of the digital detector, the characteristic of the latter follows the "Ideal RMS, RC-averaging" line of Fig.3.70 for all values of $T_E/T_A < 0,1$ (when exponential averaging is used). For values between 0,1 and 1 the dotted transition line is followed, but it is not advisable to make use of this region unless T_E is known very accurately. Conversion to energy is achieved by multiplying by $T_A/2$ as stated in Section 3.7.3.5.

2) When T_{Eo} is governed by filter response time rather than the length of the transient itself then combination of Eqn.(3.45) ($T_{Eo} \approx 1/B$) with the requirement that $T_{Eo}/T_A \leq 0,1$ results in $BT_A \geq 10$ which can be directly read off from Fig.4.17. This figure thus indicates directly the lowest frequency for which this method is valid for each averaging time.

3) Account must be taken of the fact that in "Max. Hold" mode the detector output is only sampled every 22 ms, but this is less of a problem than may at first appear. The maximum rate of fall of the detector is $8,7\,dB/T_A$ and thus for $T_A = 0,25\,s$ the maximum error will be $< 0,8\,dB$ (and halved for each doubling of T_A). It is unlikely that T_A will be required less than 0,25 s because even in that case, Fig.4.17 indicates that the analysis is only valid for frequencies of 200 Hz and above.

4.7.3. Analysis using Linear Averaging

This is a possibility which was not discussed in Section 3.7 because most analog detectors perform exponential integration.

Linear integration (over the whole transient) corresponds to the line for "Linear Integration" in Fig.3.70 and is very straightforward. Conversion to energy is achieved by multiplying directly by the linear integration time.

In order to optimise the dynamic range it is necessary for the averaging time to be as short as possible with respect to the length of the transient. Thus in comparison with the method of Section 4.7.2 it suffers from the disadvantage of having to trigger the integration at the correct time. In fact to minimise the averaging time it may be necessary to trigger the generation of the transient to be analyzed from the start of an averaging cycle. Note that the filter response time (Section 3.7.2.2) must be added to the length of the input transient.

184

5. FAST FOURIER TRANSFORM (FFT)

As mentioned in Section 2.2.4 the Fast Fourier Transform (FFT) is an algorithm or calculation procedure for obtaining the Discrete Fourier Transform (DFT) with a greatly reduced number of arithmetic operations compared with a direct evaluation. Since its first publication in 1965 (Ref.5.1) it has revolutionized the field of signal analysis, and it is currently without a doubt the most important single analysis technique available. At first the algorithm was implemented on large computers in

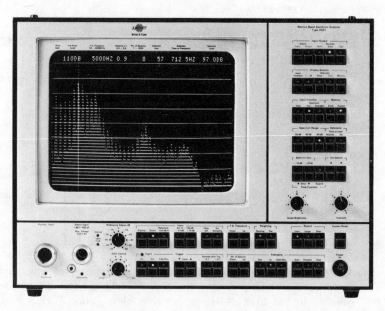

Fig.5.1. Narrow Band Spectrum Analyzer Type 2031

a high-level language such as FORTRAN, later in assembler language on mini-computers. Current trends are to dedicated hardware implementations for high real-time frequency, and micro-processor firmware for low-cost stand-alone analyzers with more modest real-time capabilities. The B & K Analyzer Type 2031 (Fig.5.1) represents this latter possibility.

One of the major advantages of the FFT over other types of frequency analysis, e. g. by time compression, is that retention of phase information makes transformation in either direction possible and in fact relatively simple. It also permits the evaluation of a large number of functions applicable to multi-channel measurements, e. g. correlation, coherence, transfer functions, etc. In this chapter, the discussion is limited to frequency analysis of single channel signals, but the other functions are treated briefly in the next chapter on Advanced Analysis.

5.1. THE FFT ALGORITHM

For convenience, the basic equations of the DFT (from Section 2.2.4) will be repeated here. In particular, the DFT (forward and inverse transforms) are represented by:

$$G(k) = \frac{1}{N} \sum_{n=0}^{N-1} g(n)e^{-j\frac{2\pi kn}{N}} \qquad (2.18)$$

$$g(n) = \sum_{k=0}^{N-1} G(k)e^{j\frac{2\pi kn}{N}} \qquad (2.19)$$

while a matrix version of Eqn.(2.18) for N = 8 is represented by:

$$
\begin{bmatrix} G_0 \\ G_1 \\ G_2 \\ G_3 \\ G_4 \\ G_5 \\ G_6 \\ G_7 \end{bmatrix}
= \frac{1}{8}
\begin{bmatrix}
\uparrow & \uparrow & \uparrow & \uparrow & \uparrow & \uparrow & \uparrow & \uparrow \\
\uparrow & \nearrow & \rightarrow & \searrow & \downarrow & \swarrow & \leftarrow & \nwarrow \\
\uparrow & \rightarrow & \downarrow & \leftarrow & \uparrow & \rightarrow & \downarrow & \leftarrow \\
\uparrow & \searrow & \leftarrow & \nearrow & \uparrow & \nwarrow & \rightarrow & \swarrow \\
\uparrow & \downarrow & \uparrow & \downarrow & \uparrow & \downarrow & \uparrow & \downarrow \\
\uparrow & \swarrow & \rightarrow & \nwarrow & \downarrow & \nearrow & \leftarrow & \searrow \\
\uparrow & \leftarrow & \downarrow & \rightarrow & \uparrow & \leftarrow & \downarrow & \rightarrow \\
\uparrow & \nwarrow & \leftarrow & \swarrow & \downarrow & \searrow & \rightarrow & \nearrow
\end{bmatrix}
\begin{bmatrix} g_0 \\ g_1 \\ g_2 \\ g_3 \\ g_4 \\ g_5 \\ g_6 \\ g_7 \end{bmatrix}
\qquad (2.20a)
$$

The advantages of the FFT can be achieved in a veriety of ways and for different radix number systems (Ref.5.2, 4.1) but the discussion here will be limited to a particular version of a Radix 2 algorithm, where N is a power of 2. The differences between the different versions are of a secondary nature and of most interest to an instrument designer rather than user. However, it is probably of interest to a user to know roughly how the FFT algorithm functions, so as to be able to appreciate any restrictions in its applicability.

Basically, the savings of the FFT algorithm result from factorizing the **A** matrix of Eqn.(2.20a) into a number *(log$_2$ N)* of individual matrices. This does not immediately appear to give any benefit, but it will be shown that the factor matrices contain only two non-zero elements in each row, of which one is always unity, so that multiplication by each of the factor matrices requires only *N* complex multiplications. The total number of multiplications is thus of the order of *N log$_2$ N* instead of the *N^2* required to multiply by the **A** matrix in one step. As mentioned in Section 2.2.4 this represents a saving by a factor of 100 for the typical case of *N* = 1024.

In fact it is not the matrix **A** directly which is factorized, but a reshuffled version of it which is illustrated in Fig.5.2, and which will be called **B**. Matrix **B** is obtained from **A** by interchanging the rows with those of "bit-reversed address", i.e. the binary representation of the row numbers 0 to 7 (000 to 111) is reversed end-for-end to obtain the new address. Symmetrical numbers such as 101 remain unchanged. In Fig.5.2, on the left-hand-side, the actual row numbers are given in bi-

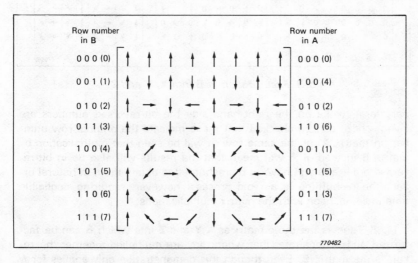

770482

Fig.5.2. Matrix **B** *(***A** *with rows reshuffled to bit-reversed address)*

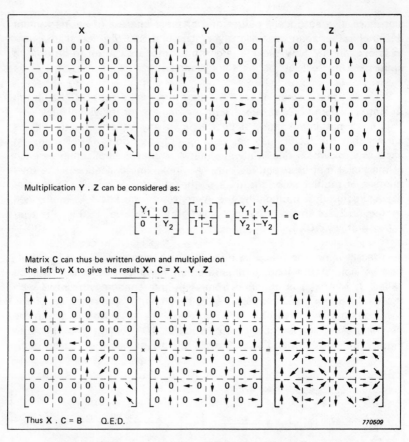

770509

Multiplication **Y** . **Z** can be considered as:

$$\begin{bmatrix} Y_1 & 0 \\ 0 & Y_2 \end{bmatrix} \begin{bmatrix} I & I \\ I & -I \end{bmatrix} = \begin{bmatrix} Y_1 & Y_1 \\ Y_2 & -Y_2 \end{bmatrix} = C$$

Matrix **C** can thus be written down and multiplied on the left by **X** to give the result **X** . **C** = **X** . **Y** . **Z**

Thus **X** . **C** = **B**   Q.E.D.

*Fig.5.3. Factorization of **B** into **X**, **Y** and **Z***

nary form, while on the right-hand side the bit-reversed numbers are given, and it can be checked that these indicate the original row number (in matrix **A**) of the same row. It will be seen that multiplication by matrix **B** instead of **A** will mean that the results will also be in bit-reversed order and will have to be reshuffled to obtain them in natural order. The reshuffling is a rapid process, however, requiring negligible time in comparison with the matrix multiplications.

Fig.5.3 shows the three matrices **X**,**Y** and **Z** into which **B** can be factorized, and demonstrates that when they are multiplied together the result is the matrix **B**. Even though this demonstration only applies for N = 8, it will be appreciated that the same principles can be extended to values of *N* equal to any power of 2. As an example of the systematic nature of the factor matrices, it will be seen that the upper left quadrant of matrix **Y** (submatrix **Y₁**) is a copy of matrix **Z** but of order $N/2$. The upper left submatrix of matrix **X** is the next smaller version of the same matrix, having the general form:

$$\begin{bmatrix} I & I \\ I & -I \end{bmatrix}$$

Each successive matrix (in the order **Z**, **Y**, **X**) introduces progressively smaller rotations; **Z** involves only 1/2 revolutions, **Y** introduces 1/4 revolutions while it is only at the last stage that 1/8 revolutions are introduced.

Fig.5.4 shows another representation of the same algorithm, this time indicating the way in which the successive multiplications by the factor matrices **Z**, **Y** and **X** can actually be carried out in a computer. It will be seen that the whole operation can be done "in place", i. e., the result of each step is stored in the same memory locations as the original data (and thus so is the final result).

At each step the data values can always be operated on pairwise, the results of the operation being placed back in the memory locations of the 2 data values from which they were obtained. It can easily be checked that the first three steps in the diagram of Fig.5.4 correspond to multiplication by the matrices **Z**, **Y** and **X**, respectively, while the final step represents the reshuffling to bit-reversed addresses.

A practical point is that multiplication by a unit vector with a given orientation involves multiplications by the sine and cosine coefficients of that angle. Considerable time can be saved by having these sine values tabulated, rather than generating them repeatedly, although this of course requires more memory space. However, for a transform of size *N* it is only necessary to store $N/4$ sine coefficients since all values can be simply generated from those for the first quarter period. Moreover, both sine and cosine coefficients can be generated from the same table.

5.2. THE FFT FOR REAL-VALUED SERIES

Thus far, no distinction has been made between the time samples $g(n)$ and the frequency spectrum values $G(k)$, but in the most common

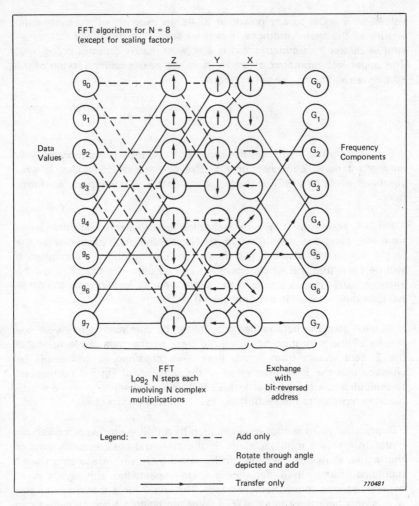

Fig.5.4. Flow diagram for FFT algorithm

practical situation the *g(n)* values will be real while the *G(k)* values will be complex. The FFT algorithm so far discussed is equally valid for real or complex data. If applied to real data, however, there will be two redundancies:

1. The imaginary part of each input data value will be zero and thus half the memory will be used for storing zeroes.

2. The second half of the resulting spectrum, i. e. the frequencies from f_N to f_s, also represent the negative frequencies from $-f_N$ to zero (Fig.2.6) and since the latter are the complex conjugates of the positive frequencies (Eqn.(2.12)) there is no need to store them separately.

It is possible to remove these redundancies by means of an algorithm which transforms a number N of real values as though they were $N/2$ complex values and then manipulates the result to obtain the first half of the spectrum of the original real data points (Ref.5.3). Most FFT systems operate in this manner. It should be noted that because of the antisymmetry of the imaginary components of the spectra of real functions both the zero frequency (DC) and Nyquist frequency components are real numbers and in fact appear as the real and imaginary components, respectively, of the first complex number of the output spectrum (Fig.5.5). All the other complex numbers are genuine frequency components distributed linearly with frequency up to $f_N \times (N{-}2)/N$ i. e. just less than the Nyquist frequency. It is possible to move the Nyquist frequency component to its correct position at the end of the table, but this then requires $(N/2 + 1)$ (complex) storage locations. It is in any case not usually necessary, since to avoid aliasing it is desirable for the Nyquist frequency component to be zero, or at least so small that it is not usable.

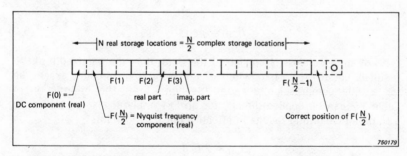

Fig.5.5. Arrangement of output array from FFT algorithm for N real-valued samples

5.3. DETERMINATION OF ANALYSIS PARAMETERS

5.3.1. Frequency Range

As just described, the frequency range is always from zero (DC) to the Nyquist frequency f_N (i. e. one half of the sampling frequency f_s) independent of the number of samples in the data record. Usually, low-pass filters are used to guard against aliasing, and since the whole spectrum up to f_N is calculated in any case, it is desirable to place the cutoff frequency of the lowpass filters as close as possible to this. It is feasible using filters with a roll-off of 113 dB/octave to utilize almost 80% of the calculated values, while still retaining a dynamic range of 72 dB in the useful frequency range.●

5.3.2. Resolution β

Defining this as the frequency increment between lines in the spectrum, this is related to the number of samples in the original time series (N) as follows:

$$\beta = \frac{f_s}{N} = \frac{2f_N}{N} \tag{5.1}$$

5.3.3. Bandwidth B

The bandwidth is determined by the resolution and by any time-weighting function (time window) applied to the data. For linearly weighted data the effective noise bandwidth is equal to the resolution, i.e.

$$B_{eff} = \beta \tag{5.2}$$

If any time window is applied to the data, then the bandwidth of the result is equal to the bandwidth of the weighting function, exactly as for a time compression analyzer (Section 3.5.4). The information of Table 3.7 can be applied directly for an FFT analyzer also. In particular a Hanning weighting results in effective noise bandwidth:

$$B_{eff} = 1{,}5\ \beta \tag{5.3}$$

One means of obtaining a finer resolution without changing the bandwidth is to add zeroes to the data record, but this is of course at the expense of a larger transform size and time. For example, if a record of length N is extended to $2N$ with zeroes and a transform of size $2N$ performed, then the resolution will be $f_s/2N$ while the bandwidth will still

---

● For example the B & K Analyzer Type 2031 transforms 1024 real data points to obtain 512 frequency lines, of which 400 are valid and are displayed

be f_s/N (Fig.5.6). This can of course be interpreted as applying a rectangular weighting function of length N to a data record of length $2N$.

5.3.4. Dynamic Range

This is determined by the valid number of bits with which the input data are represented, and by the number of bits used in the calculations. As a rough rule-of-thumb one obtains 6 dB dynamic range for every bit of the input data, and thus A/D conversion with 12 bits gives about 72 dB. This dynamic range is generally not affected by the FFT calculation if 4 additional bits (i. e. 16 bits) are used in the arithmetic operations (on linear values). Some reduction of quantisation noise and increase in dynamic range is achieved by averaging.

Ref.4.1 has a detailed discussion of the effects of quantisation.

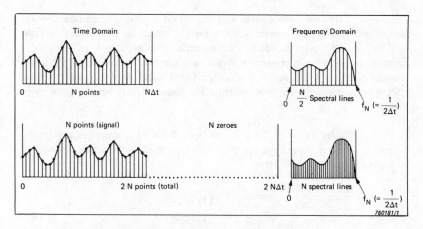

Fig.5.6. Effect of extending record with zeroes

5.4. CALIBRATION OF RESULTS

As discussed in Section 2.2.4, the DFT assumes that the signal is periodic with a period equal to the record length. The result obtained (as illustrated in Fig.5.5) represents the positive half of the 2-sided spectrum and thus must be modified as follows:

The DC component (with the same units as the input data) can be

193

taken directly from its location as indicated in Fig.5.5. All other frequency components $G(f_k)$ have a real and imaginary part and may thus be represented by:

$$G(f_k) = a_k + jb_k \qquad (5.4)$$

Thus, taking the negative frequency component into account the RMS value corresponding to $G(f_k)$ is given by:

$$G_{RMS}(f_k) = \sqrt{2(a_k{}^2 + b_k{}^2)} \qquad (5.5)$$

The power spectrum components are given by the squares of these RMS values.

5.4.1. Stationary Deterministic Signals

It is only in very few cases that the input signal will satisfy the assumption that it is periodic with a period equal to the record length, and usually it is best to apply a time window when analyzing stationary signals, in order to improve the effective filter characteristic. The discussion of Section 3.6.5 applies equally in this case, and it is thus necessary to compensate for the attenuation factor given by the time window.

The particular form of Eqn.(3.28) applicable to a discrete weighting function $W(n)$ extending over N_w samples and with a peak value of unity is:

$$F_a = \frac{\sum\limits_{n=0}^{N_w-1} |W(n)|^2}{N} \qquad (5.6)$$

where the transform size N is $\geqslant N_w$.

5.4.2. Stationary Random Signals

Exactly as for time compression analysis (Section 3.5.4) the BT product associated with each transform is 1 and thus the statistical accuracy can be improved by averaging over several records, the BT product for insertion in Eqn.(3.9) ($\epsilon = 1/(2\sqrt{BT})$) being equal to the number of independent records over which the average is made. Another possibil-

194

ity is to increase B by averaging over a number of adjacent frequency components.

In this case the BT product is given by the number of original bandwidths in the integrated bandwidth (and thus in the case of weighted functions not necessarily equal to the number of spectral lines integrated). Normally the first method is preferable, but the second does give an improvement in the relative steepness of filter characteristic which may be desirable in certain situations.

Where a time-weighting function is used, the power spectrum levels should be compensated by the attenuation factor of Eqn.(5.6) and in order to convert the results to a power spectral density it is necessary to divide the power spectrum values by the effective bandwidth of the weighting function (Table 3.7). This is also the same as for the Time Compression Analysis discussed in Section 3.5.4.1.

5.4.3. Transient Signals

As for Time Compression Analysis, the discussion of Section 3.7.1.4 also applies here.

If the whole transient can be contained in one record of length N samples, then the power spectrum (of the assumed periodically repeated transient) obtained as in Section 5.4.1 (though with rectangular weighting) can be converted to an energy spectrum by multiplying by the time corresponding to the record length, i. e. $N\Delta t$ or N/f_s. The energy spectrum can be converted to an energy spectral density by dividing by the bandwidth (and thus for rectangular weighting, the line spacing β).

If the transient is longer than the record length then it is still possible to analyze it, though with the following restrictions:

1. A linear average over a number of consecutive spectra will give a correct energy spectrum provided the analysis is truly real-time (i. e. the successive time records contiguous). The time with which the power spectrum should be multiplied is the total linear averaging time.

2. Linear weighting should be used because in general the transient will be non-stationary along each record. The bandwidth and filter characteristic of the analysis will thus be determined by the rectan-

gular window of length N, and therefore relatively poor.

3. Because the analysis bandwidth is determined by the record length of N samples (which is shorter than the transient) it is possible for it to be greater than that of the transient and thus conversion to an energy spectral density may not be valid.

6. ADVANCED ANALYSIS

It is the intention in this chapter to give a brief introduction to a number of topics which, although perhaps known for a considerable time, have only become widely applicable since the advent of FFT techniques. The first few topics, viz. Zoom FFT, autocorrelation, power cepstrum and complex cepstrum, are applicable to the analysis of single channel signals, while the remaining topics, viz. cross correlation, cross spectra, transfer function analysis and coherence are applicable to the analysis of multiple channel signals.

As far as possible the principles developed in Chapter 2 are used in the explanations. The discussion is intended as an introduction only; very few practical details are given. On the other hand, references are given to enable the reader to follow up most topics in more detail.

6.1. ZOOM FFT

As discussed in Chapter 5, the result of a normal FFT analysis is distributed in frequency from zero up to the Nyquist frequency f_N, and the frequency resolution is determined by the number of frequency lines up to f_N (normally half the number of original data samples). In certain situations it is desirable to obtain a considerably finer resolution over a limited portion of the spectrum, and the so-called "Zoom-FFT" procedure permits this. It can be considered as "zooming in" on a limited portion of the spectrum with a resolution power corresponding to the number of lines normally used for the whole spectrum (Fig.6.1).

6.1.1. Principle of Operation

In Section 2.2.1, in the discussion of how the Fourier integral (Eqn.(2.10)) functions, it was mentioned that multiplication by a rotat-

197

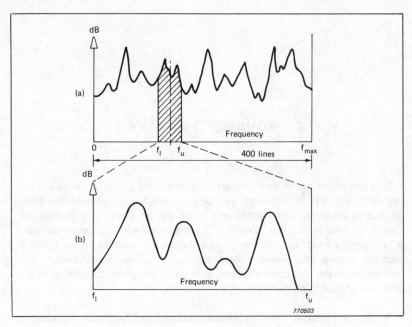

Fig.6.1. (a) Original 400-line spectrum
(b) Shaded section of (a) "zoomed" by factor 10:1

ing unit vector $e^{-j2\pi f_k t}$ effectively shifts the frequency origin to frequency f_k. The component at frequency f_k is stopped in the position it occupied at time zero, and virtually becomes a new DC component (although in general it is complex). The positive and negative sampling frequencies $\pm f_s$ are likewise moved by an amount f_k, as illustrated in Fig.6.2. (This may introduce aliasing in the negative frequency region, as the new negative Nyquist frequency $(-f_N + f_k)$ may lie higher in frequency than the lowest frequency component.) Note that even if the original time signal $g(t)$ were real, the modified signal would be a sequence of complex values.

It is thus possible by multiplying any time signal $g(t)$ by a unit vector rotating at $-f_k$ to change its frequency origin to frequency f_k. The complex signal, thus modified, can then be low-pass filtered (using a digital filter) to remove all frequency components except for a narrow band around f_k, as illustrated in Fig.6.2. Note that at the same time this lowpass filtration would generally remove the portion of the spectrum where aliasing may have occurred. The narrow frequency band remaining after lowpass filtration (the shaded area in Fig.6.2) is shown to a

198

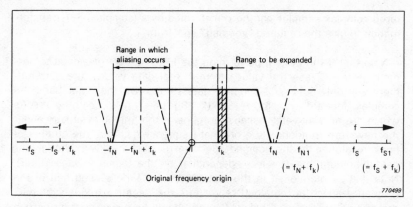

Fig.6.2. Frequency shift caused by multiplying signal by unit vector rotating at $-f_k$

larger scale in Fig.6.3 where it is also made apparent that it is now possible to reduce the sampling frequency while still complying with the sampling theorem. For example, if the total bandwidth after filtering is less than 1/10 of the sampling frequency, it is possible to reduce the sampling frequency to 1/10 without overlapping in the vicinity of the new Nyquist frequency. In a similar manner to the digital filters discussed in Chapter 4, the reduction in sampling frequency is achieved simply by retaining a reduced number of samples, in this case every tenth, the rest being discarded. The resampled sequence of lowpass-fil-

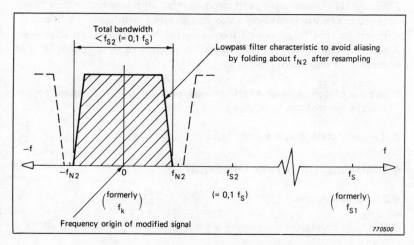

Fig.6.3. Detail of range to be expanded after resampling

199

tered complex samples can be transformed by a (complex) FFT transformation to give the required "zoomed" spectrum.

Note that if the system performing the FFT has been designed to normally give $N/2$ spectral values from N real data values, the data memory will only hold $N/2$ complex data values. On the other hand the complex forward transform (Eqn.(2.18)) gives $N/2$ complex results which are now all valid, because in general there is no symmetry about the new zero frequency (the original frequency f_k). Thus the number of lines resolution in the zoomed spectrum is unchanged● (although the useful amount may be less, depending on the digital lowpass filter). Note that as mentioned in the footnote on p.17 the second half of the frequency spectrum obtained represents the negative frequencies (i.e. the original frequencies below f_k) and should be moved to their correct position before the first half prior to display.

6.1.2. Applications of Zoom FFT

Zoom FFT is useful wherever it is desired to have a fine resolution without increasing the transform size, e. g.

1. In signals with relatively low frequency modulations resulting in sidebands with a spacing equal to the modulating frequency. Gearbox and ball-bearing spectra provide typical examples (Refs.6.1, 6.2).

2. In signals containing a very large number of harmonics. Once again gearbox vibrations provide an example, since with certain tooth combinations, the fundamental frequency (of contact between any given pair of teeth) may be very low with respect to both rotational and meshing frequencies (Ref.6.1).

3. Where closely spaced sharp resonances are not adequately separated by normal analysis.

4. To define details in a steeply sloping phase spectrum.

6.2. AUTOCORRELATION FUNCTION

6.2.1. Introduction

The autocorrelation function gives a measure of the extent to which a

---
● To obtain a zoom factor of 10 the sample rate must be changed by a factor of 20

signal correlates with a displaced version of itself, as a function of the displacement.

The autocorrelation $R_{xx}(\tau)$ of a function $f_x(t)$ is defined by the equation:

$$R_{xx}(\tau) = \lim_{T \to \infty} \frac{1}{T} \int_{-T/2}^{T/2} f_x(t) \quad f_x(t + \tau) \, dt \qquad (6.1)$$

It can be seen that the value for $\tau = 0$ (the maximum value) is simply the mean square value of $f_x(t)$. The autocorrelation function is often normalized to a maximum value of 1 by dividing through by the mean square value.

It is a well-known fact (the so-called Wiener-Khinchin relations) that the power spectrum is the forward Fourier transform of the autocorrelation function, and this can readily be understood as follows:

By comparison of Eqn.(6.1) with a version of the Convolution Equation (2.28) viz.

$$g(\tau) = \int_{-\infty}^{\infty} f(t)h(-t + \tau) \, dt \qquad (6.2)$$

it can be seen that Eqn.(6.1) virtually represents the convolution of $f_x(t)$ and $f_x(-t)$ (i.e. the same signal reversed in time). The normalising factor $1/T$ in Eqn.(6.1) is required for stationary signals, but not for transients with a finite total energy, to which the Fourier Integral Transform of Eqn.(2.14) applies.

From the Convolution Theorem of Section 2.5.3 the convolution represented by Eqn.(6.1) thus transforms in the frequency domain to a product. Letting

$$\mathscr{F}\{f_x(t)\} = F_x(f)$$

then $\qquad \mathscr{F}\{f_x(-t)\} = F_x(-f)$ (because if time runs backwards, vectors

$$= F_x^*(f) \qquad \text{rotate backwards)} \qquad (6.3)$$

from Eqn.(2.12)

Thus, $\qquad \mathscr{F}\{R_{xx}(\tau)\} = \mathscr{F}\{f_x(t)\} \cdot \mathscr{F}\{f_x(-t)\}$

$$= F_x(f) \cdot F_x^*(f)$$

$$= |F_x(f)|^2 \qquad (6.4)$$

201

the power spectrum of $f_x(t)$

This relationship was at one time widely used to obtain the power spectrum by digital means. Since the advent of the FFT, however, the situation has been reversed and the autocorrelation function can now be most rapidly obtained by inverse transformation of the power spectrum, itself obtained by forward transformation of the original time signal.

When using the DFT, however, the procedure is not completely straightforward because of the implicit periodicity already referred to. The inverse transform of a simple power spectrum would be the autocorrelation of the periodic signal obtained by joining the original signal sample into an endless loop. To avoid this "folding back" it is desirable to add N zeroes to a data record of length N (before transforming it) in order to obtain N time shifts without the effect of foldback. From Fig.6.4 it can be seen that the introduction of the zeroes reduces the range of non-zero products with increasing displacement, and in order to obtain unbiased results, comparable with those which would be obtained from a continuous stationary signal, it is necessary to divide the

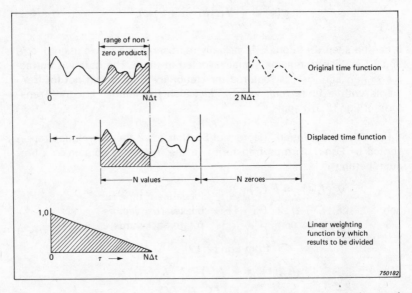

Fig.6.4. Addition of zeroes to avoid "wrap-around" in correlation estimates

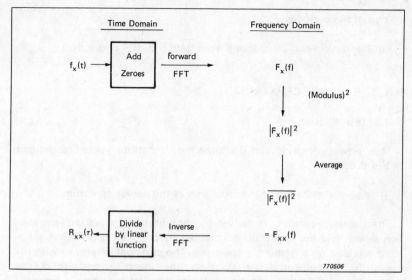

Fig.6.5. Calculating autocorrelation using FFT

results by a factor decreasing linearly from 1 at zero displacement to zero at N displacements (Fig.6.4). Evidently the inaccuracy increases with τ and only the first half or 3/4 of these results will be valid.

Fig.6.5 illustrates schematically a procedure for calculating the autocorrelation function, making use of an FFT algorithm for forward and inverse transformation.

6.2.2. Applications

Among the applications of the autocorrelation function are:

1. The detection of echoes in a signal and measurement of their strength and associated time delays. It appears that the cepstrum (see later) may be more suitable for this because it is less sensitive to the bandwidth of the power spectrum.

2. The detection of periodicity buried in noise, since the autocorrelation of a periodic signal is also periodic whereas that of noise falls rapidly to zero with increasing time displacement. The power spectrum may be more suitable for this because it also gives the frequency distribu-

203

tion of the periodicity.

Further details can be obtained from Refs.6.3, 6.4 and 6.5.

6.3. THE POWER CEPSTRUM

6.3.1. Introduction

The "power cepstrum" (at that time the "cepstrum") was first defined in Ref.6.6 as:

"The power spectrum of the *logarithm* of the power spectrum."

The name "cepstrum" is derived by paraphrasing "spectrum" the reason being that the cepstrum is obtained by performing a further spectrum analysis on a frequency spectrum. The principal difference with respect to the autocorrelation function (the inverse transform of the power spectrum) is that for the cepstrum the first spectrum is logarithmically converted (i. e. in dB).

The name "power cepstrum" is now used to distinguish this function from the "complex cepstrum" discussed in Section 6.4.

Mathematically, if the forward Fourier transform of a time function $f_x(t)$ is denoted by:

$$F_x(f) = \mathscr{F}\{f_x(t)\} \qquad (6.5)$$

then the power spectrum may be represented by:

$$F_{xx}(f) = |F_x(f)|^2 \qquad (6.6)$$

and the cepstrum by:

$$C_x(\tau) = |\mathscr{F}\{log[F_{xx}(f)]\}|^2 \qquad (6.7)$$

Note that the autocorrelation function may be represented as:

$$R_{xx}(\tau) = \mathscr{F}^{-1}\{F_{xx}(f)\} \qquad (6.8)$$

The independent variable "τ" of the cepstrum was termed the "Quefrency" by Bogert et al. (Ref.6.6), though it has the dimensions of time

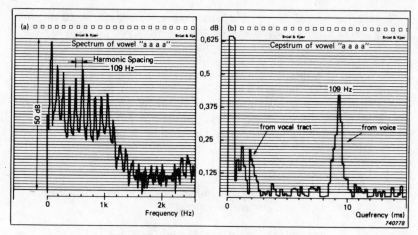

Fig.6.6. (a) Spectrum of vowel "aaaa"
(b) Cepstrum from Fig.6.6(a)

and is virtually the same as the "τ" of the autocorrelation function. The terminology is probably useful for those used to interpreting time signals in terms of their frequency components, since a high quefrency represents a rapid fluctuation in the spectrum and a low quefrency a slow one, and so on. Bogert et al. proposed a number of other paraphrased terms, such as "Rahmonic" (from Harmonic), "Lifter" (from Filter) etc., but the survival of these is somewhat more dubious.

Bogert et al.'s application of the cepstrum was concerned with the detection of echo delay times in seismic signals containing an echo, and for this purpose it was claimed to have advantages over the autocorrelation function. These are presumably due to the fact that, as Trampe Broch has shown for the cross correlation function (Ref.6.7), the detection of peaks corresponding to echoes is very dependent on the shape of the frequency spectrum, and is virtually impossible after filtering (which would for example occur by transmission through the earth). The logarithm of the power spectrum, on the other hand, is nowhere near so sensitive to the bandwidth of this filtering, and the cepstrum was shown to give evidence of delay peaks even where these were not distinguishable in the autocorrelation.

This lack of sensitivity to the global shape of a spectrum was later realised to have wider applications, of which one of the major ones is typified by its use in speech analysis (Ref.6.8).

205

Fig.6.6(a) shows a frequency analysis (on a logarithmic or dB amplitude scale) of a typical vowel sound. The spectrum will be seen to have two major characteristics, a large number of harmonic components with a spacing equal to the voice pitch, and a number of resonant peaks, so-called formants, which are determined by the shape of the vocal tract and which define the particular vowel sound. Representing the power spectrum of the original voice signal by *V(f)*, and the global shape of the resonance (formant) characteristic by *F(f)*, the *power spectrum* of the resulting vowel sound will be seen to be

$$S(f) = V(f) \cdot F(f) \qquad (6.9)$$

In the logarithmic representation shown, however, the product transforms to an addition, and one can write that

$$log[S(f)] = log[V(f)] + log[F(f)] \qquad (6.10)$$

Because of the linearity of the Fourier transform, this additive relationship is maintained in the cepstrum

$$\text{ie.} \mathscr{F}\{log\ S\} = \mathscr{F}\{log\ V\} + \mathscr{F}\{log\ F\} \qquad (6.11)$$

The result of doing this is shown in Fig.6.6(b), and it can be seen that because the voice and formant characteristics have vastly different "quefrency" contents in the spectrum, the two effects have become completely separated in the cepstrum. This useful example is not limited to speech analysis. The function *V(f)* could equally well represent the spectrum of an internal source in a machine, and *F(f)* the transfer function from the source to an external measurement point.

If the quefrency content of the interesting features of the source spectrum is well separated from that of the transfer function, the interesting part of the cepstrum will be little affected by the overall shape of the spectrum and thus be reasonably independent of the particular measuring point.

A further advantage of the cepstrum is its ability to detect and give a measure of phenomena which exhibit periodicity in the spectrum, such as harmonics and sidebands. In particular, in complex signals containing a mixture of different families of harmonics and/or sidebands, the separation of the various periodicities is greatly facilitated by performing the second Fourier transform to obtain the cepstrum.

It is worthwhile to discuss the units of the cepstrum. Since the logarithmic spectrum is usually expressed in dB, it is natural to express the cepstrum values as (dB)^2. The author in fact prefers the *amplitude* spectrum to the power spectrum for the second transform, in which case the results are scaled in dB. Another point is whether the second transform should be a forward or inverse transform (some people specify the latter) but in fact it is not important, since the result is identical except for a scaling factor, and it is only necessary that consistency is maintained. It is somewhat more efficient to use two forward transforms since the second one need only be half the size of the first.

6.3.2. Applications of the Power Cepstrum

1. The detection of echoes in a signal and measurement of their delay time (Ref. 6.6, 6.9).

2. In speech analysis, for detecting voiced sounds and giving a measure of voice pitch (Ref. 6.8).

3. For detecting harmonic patterns in machine vibration spectra e. g. for detecting blade failure in turbines (Ref. 6.10).

4. For detecting and separating families of sidebands in a spectrum, e. g. those indicating faults in gearboxes (Ref. 6.11).

6.4. THE COMPLEX CEPSTRUM

6.4.1. Introduction

Another type of cepstrum, known as the "Complex Cepstrum", is described in Ref. 6.12. Despite its name it is a real-valued function, but the name indicates that, unlike the power cepstrum, the complex cepstrum is obtained from the complex spectrum, with no loss of phase information. For this reason the process by which it is obtained is reversible, and it is thus possible to return to the original signal after performing filtering operations. It will be seen that this allows the removal of convolved and multiplied effects by linear filtering techniques.

The complex cepstrum is defined as "the inverse Fourier transform of the complex logarithm of the complex spectrum (the forward Fourier transform of the time signal)".

Mathematically, if $F_x(f)$ as defined in Equation (6.5) is expressed in the form $A(f)e^{j\phi(f)}$, i.e. in terms of its amplitude and phase instead of its real and imaginary parts, then the complex logarithm of this can be written as:

$$L(f) = LnA(f) + j\phi(f) \qquad (6.12)$$

The complex cepstrum is then defined as:

$$K(\tau) = \mathscr{F}^{-1}\{L(f)\} \qquad (6.13)$$

The phase function $\phi(f)$ must be made continuous (rather than its principle value modulo 2π) in order that $L(f)$ has the property that (complex) multiplications in $F_x(f)$ transform to additions in $L(f)$; thus, effects which are convolved in the original time signal now become additive in the complex logarithm of the spectrum and remain so in the complex cepstrum.

It is a simple matter to show that the complex cepstrum is a real-valued function. If the time signal $f_x(t)$ is real-valued, the complex spectrum $F_x(f)$ is conjugate even (i.e. real parts even, imaginary parts odd). It follows directly that the amplitude function $A(f)$ and log amplitude $LnA(f)$ are also even, and phase function $\phi(f)$ odd. Thus the complex function $L(f)$ is conjugate even, and transforms by the inverse Fourier transform to a real-valued function in the time domain.

Not only may effects now be separated in the complex cepstrum, but it is possible to remove one completely, and return to the original time signal without this effect. This opens the possibility of negating the effect of a signal transmission path by subtracting the complex cepstrum of its transfer function from the complex cepstrum of the measured signal in order to obtain the signal at the source. The advantages of doing this in the cepstrum rather than the spectrum are:

1. It is only necessary to operate on one function rather than on amplitude and phase separately.

2. The transfer function would often be low quefrency and would thus only need to be removed over a limited range of the cepstrum.

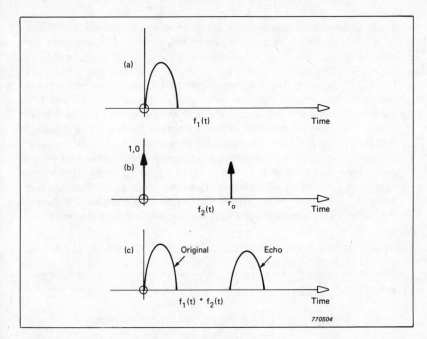

Fig.6.7. Signal with echo as a convolution with two delta functions

6.4.2. Applications

1. Deconvolution as described above. Ref.4.1, for example, describes its use for the improvement of old acoustic recordings, basically by removing the influence of the recording horn.

2. Echo Removal. A signal containing an echo can be considered as the convolution of the original function with two delta functions, one located at zero time and one delayed by τ_o (with reduced amplitude corresponding to the attenuation of the echo). Fig.6.7 illustrates this. This convolution transforms by the forward Fourier transform to a multiplication of the original spectrum with that of the pair of delta functions. The latter consists of a uniform level with an additive rotating vector, the period in the frequency spectrum of one rotation being equal to $1/\tau_o$. (Because of the symmetry of the Fourier transform pair this is virtually the same as would be obtained in the time domain by inverse transformation of a frequency spectrum consisting of two delta functions as in Fig.6.7(b).) On taking logarithms, the

209

multiplication becomes an addition (both in log amplitude and phase) of a function which is periodic (though distorted) with the same period $1/\tau_0$.

Fig.6.8 illustrates this for the specific case of a damped sinusoid with two equispaced echoes. The additive periodicity referred to is evident in both the log amplitude and phase spectra (Fig.6.8 b & c resp.). By inverse transformation to obtain the complex cepstrum (Fig.6.8d) the periodicity transforms to a number of delta functions with spacing τ_0 (the multiplicity being partly due to the two echoes and partly due to the distortion caused by taking logs). These delta functions contain all information about the echo, and if they are removed by a "comb" filter, the cepstrum can be transformed back to the logarithmic spectrum of Fig.6.8 e & f. An antilogarithmic conver-

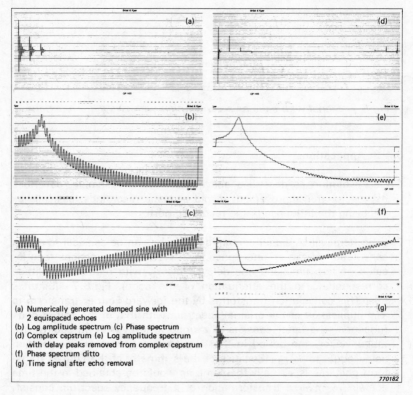

(a) Numerically generated damped sine with 2 equispaced echoes
(b) Log amplitude spectrum (c) Phase spectrum
(d) Complex cepstrum (e) Log amplitude spectrum with delay peaks removed from complex cepstrum
(f) Phase spectrum ditto
(g) Time signal after echo removal

770182

Fig.6.8. Example of echo removal by complex cepstrum

sion and further inverse transform produces the original time signal without echoes, but with a minimal loss of other information. The same procedure is effective even when there is considerable overlap of the echoes (note that the complex cepstrum is considerably shorter than the original time function).

3. Speech analysis and transmission. Refs.4.1 & 6.12 describe how the separation of speech into voice and vocal tract effects (as for the power cepstrum, Fig.6.6) allows the latter to be transmitted efficiently and used to modulate a synthetic voice (or noise source for unvoiced speech) with pitch the same as the original.

4. Analysis of seismic signals. Lowpass and highpass filtering in the complex cepstrum allow deconvolution of an original seismic wavelet from the impulse response of the earth's crust at the measurement point (Refs.6.13, 4.1).

6.5. CROSS-CORRELATION AND CROSS SPECTRUM

6.5.1. Introduction

The cross-correlation function gives a measure of the extent to which two signals correlate with each other as a function of the time displacement between them.

The cross-correlation $R_{xy}(\tau)$ of two functions $f_x(t)$ and $f_y(t)$ is defined by the equation:

$$R_{xy}(\tau) = \lim_{T \to \infty} \frac{1}{T} \int_{-T/2}^{T/2} f_x(t) \ f_y(t + \tau) \, dt \qquad (6.14)$$

The cross-correlation function can be normalized to a maximum value of 1 by dividing through by $\sqrt{R_{xx}(o) \cdot R_{yy}(o)}$, the product of the RMS values of the two signals. $R_{xy}(\tau)$ of course reduces to the autocorrelation when $f_x(t) = f_y(t)$.

The cross-spectrum $F_{xy}(f)$ of $f_x(t)$ and $f_y(t)$ is the forward Fourier transform of the cross-correlation function $R_{xy}(\tau)$ and since the latter is not an even function (as is the autocorrelation function) the cross-spectrum is in general complex. The spectrum of real parts is known as the "Cospectrum" and that of imaginary parts as the "Quad-spectrum".

The cross-spectrum can alternatively be obtained from the individual Fourier spectra $F_x(f)$ and $F_y(f)$ as follows:

$$F_{xy}(f) = F_x^*(f) \cdot F_y(f) \qquad (6.15)$$

where $F_{xy}(f)$ is a typical cross-spectrum component

and $F_x^*(f)$ is the complex conjugate of $F_x(f)$.

This also follows from the Convolution Theorem as for the autocorrelation function (Section 6.2.1). It will be seen that $F_{xy}(f)$ reduces to the power spectrum $|F_x(f)|^2$, when $F_y(f) = F_x(f)$.

The cross-correlation function can be obtained by inverse transformation of the cross-spectrum. As for the autocorrelation it is desirable to add zeroes to the data records and divide the results by the same linear weighting function (Fig.6.4).

Note that the above principles can be applied to transient signals (in which case the cross spectrum has the dimensions of energy rather than power, and the normalising factor $1/T$ is not required in Eqn.(6.14)). Alternatively, for stationary random signals, the cross spectrum should be averaged over several records, the co- and quad-spectra being averaged separately.

6.5.2. Applications

Among the uses of the cross-correlation are:

1. To determine to what extent a signal measured at one point originates from a particular source, and with what time delay.

2. To detect the existence of a signal (not necessarily periodic) buried in extraneous noise.

Among the uses of the cross-spectrum are:

1. The determination of transfer functions (see next section).

2. Measurement of time delays which vary with frequency since this can be obtained from the phase shift at any frequency.

Further details may be found in Refs.2.2, 6.14, 6.15.

6.6. TRANSFER FUNCTION

6.6.1. Introduction

The transfer function (strictly speaking "frequency response") is defined as the complex ratio of the output to the input of a system as a function of frequency

i. e.
$$H_{xy}(f) = \frac{F_y(f)}{F_x(f)} \qquad (6.16)$$

where $H_{xy}(f)$ is the transfer function from x to y.

$F_y(f)$ is the Fourier spectrum of the (output) signal $f_y(t)$ measured at point y

and

$F_x(f)$ is the Fourier spectrum of the (input) signal $f_x(t)$ measured at point x.

Equation (6.16) can be used directly for a single (transient) input to the system, where $F_x(f)$ and $F_y(f)$ are obtained from sample records $f_x(t)$ and $f_y(t)$ which are concurrent and extend over the entire input and output histories.

It is also of interest to develop Equation (6.16) as follows:

$$H_{xy}(f) = \frac{F_y(f)}{F_x(f)} \cdot \frac{F_x^*(f)}{F_x^*(f)} = \frac{F_{xy}(f)}{F_{xx}(f)} \qquad (6.17)$$

i. e. the transfer function is equal to the ratio of the cross spectrum between points x and y to the power spectrum at point x and in this case the respective spectra may be obtained by long term averaging of stationary signals, possibly without affecting the normal operation of the system.

In this connection, it is worth noting that even where excitations are random (and thus the phase spectra of both input and output signals random) the transfer function will often be deterministic and thus always give the same phase *difference* between input and output at the same frequency. The subtraction of phase angles results from the *division* of the two spectral functions in Eqn.(6.16) (and from the multiplication by a *complex conjugate* value in Eqn.(6.15)).

6.6.2. Applications

1. An example of the application of these procedures is in the field of mechanical impedance studies where $f_x(t)$ will typically be an input force, $f_y(t)$ the resulting velocity, $H_{xy}(f)$ the mobility, and its reciprocal the mechanical impedance of the system.

2. Another example is is in the modal analysis of structures and systems, as described in Ref.6.16.

3. A further application is the removal of a transmission path effect to obtain a source signal from a remotely measured signal (see also under "Complex Cepstrum" in Section 6.4).

4. Because of the Convolution Theorem, it is a simple matter to find the effect of different inputs on a given system by multiplication of the spectrum of the input signal by the frequency response function of the system (rather than convolving with the impulse response).

5. To obtain the impulse response of a system by inverse transformation of the frequency response function.

6.7. COHERENCE

6.7.1. Introduction

Since for systems in general it is not known to what extent $f_y(t)$ results from $f_x(t)$, it is wise in the case of cross-correlation and transfer function calculations to check the coherence, which gives a measure of the validity of that assumption.

The coherence $\gamma_{xy}(f)$ is defined by

$$\gamma_{xy}{}^2(f) = \frac{|F_{xy}(f)|^2}{F_{xx}(f)F_{yy}(f)} \tag{6.18}$$

214

where $F_{xy}(f)$ is a cross-spectrum obtained by averaging over a number of data records (i.e. Co- and Quad-spectra averaged separately) and $F_{xx}(f)$ and $F_{yy}(f)$ are power spectra also averaged over a number of data records.

The first estimate of $\gamma_{xy}(f)$ from one record of $f_x(t)$ and $f_y(t)$ will always be unity as follows:

$$F_{xy}(f) = F_x^*(f)\, F_y(f) = |F_x(f)||F_y(f)| \; \underline{/\phi_y - \phi_x}$$

$$\therefore \; |F_{xy}(f)|^2 = |F_x(f)|^2 \; |F_y(f)|^2$$

while
$$F_{xx}(f) = |F_x(f)|^2$$

and
$$F_{yy}(f) = |F_y(f)|^2$$

$$\therefore \; |F_{xy}(f)|^2 = F_{xx}(f)\, F_{yy}(f) \qquad\qquad \text{q.e.d.}$$

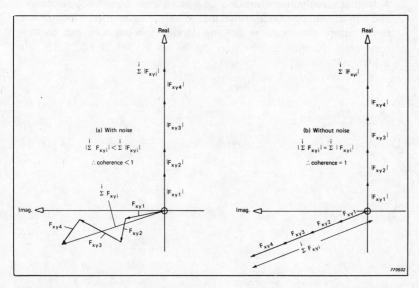

Fig.6.9. Effect of noise on modulus of averaged cross spectrum

215

However, on averaging over several records, it is only when there is no extraneous noise (i. e. the signal $f_y(t)$ stems entirely from $f_x(t)$) that the individual estimates of the cross spectrum $F_{xy}(f)$ have exactly the same angle. Fig.6.9 illustrates that it is only in this case that the vector addition used to form the mean of the cross spectrum gives the same modulus as the scalar addition of the power spectrum products.

6.7.2. Applications

1. To check the validity of cross spectra and transfer function measurements (for them to be fully valid the coherence should be 1).

2. It can be shown (e. g. Ref.6.17) that provided the signal-to-noise ratio of the measurement of the *input* signal is high, the product of the (squared) coherence and the measured output power spectrum gives a measure of the socalled "coherent output power". This is that part of the output power which is coherent with the input. This can be useful in determining the contributions of a number of independent sources to a given measured signal, for example a total noise level resulting from the addition of several significant sources.

3. A further development making use of "partial coherence functions" and "multiple coherence functions" makes possible the study of systems where the sources are no longer independent but partially correlated. Further details may be found in Refs.6.18, 6.19, and 6.20.

APPENDIX A

FOURIER ANALYSIS

(a) Integration of a vector rotated through π

Without loss of generality, the case illustrated in Fig.2.16 can be taken, where the resultant is directed along the real axis. Fig.A1 illustrates a typical component vector of length A at angle θ.

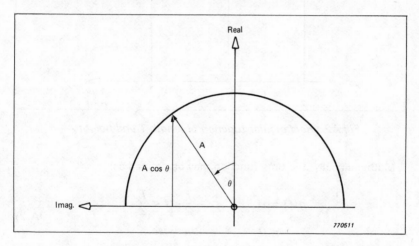

Fig.A1. Integration of a rotating vector from $-\pi/2$ to $\pi/2$

Its contribution to the resultant is $A \cos \theta$ as illustrated, and thus the average over the total angle between $-\pi/2$ and $\pi/2$ is given by

$$A_{\text{result}} = \frac{1}{\pi} \int_{-\pi/2}^{\pi/2} A \cos \theta \, d\theta \qquad (A.1)$$

217

$$= \frac{A}{\pi} \left[sin\ \theta \right]_{-\pi/2}^{\pi/2}$$

$$= \frac{2A}{\pi} \qquad \textit{as stated in Eqn. (2.21)}$$

(b) Fourier Transform of a rectangular function length T

Fig.A2 depicts a rectangular function of length T and height A, evenly divided about zero time.

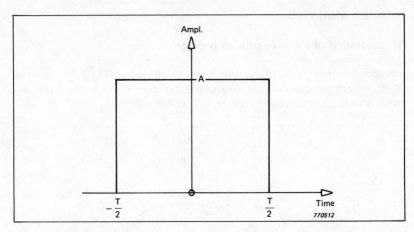

Fig.A2. Rectangular function of length T and height A

Mathematically, the time function may be defined as:

$$g(t) = A \qquad , \qquad -\frac{T}{2} < t < \frac{T}{2}$$

$$= 0 \qquad , \qquad otherwise$$

(A.2)

Thus, from Eqn. (2.14) the Fourier Transform is given by:

$$G(f) = \int_{-\infty}^{\infty} g(t)\ e^{-j2\pi ft}\ dt$$

$$= A \int_{-T/2}^{T/2} e^{-j2\pi ft}\ dt$$

218

$$= -\frac{A}{j2\pi f}\left[e^{-j2\pi ft} \right]_{-T/2}^{T/2}$$

$$= \frac{jA}{2\pi f}\left[cos(2\pi ft) - j\,sin(2\pi ft) \right]_{-T/2}^{T/2}$$

$$= AT\frac{sin(\pi fT)}{(\pi fT)} \qquad (A.3)$$

(c) Bandwidth of a sin x/x function

Fig.A.3(a) shows the amplitude characteristic corresponding to Eqn. (A.3), normalised to a peak value of unity (this can be done without loss of generality when it is the bandwidth which is required). The amplitude characteristic is thus a $|sin\ x/x|$ function where $x = \pi fT$. The amplitude squared, or power transmission characteristic is shown in Fig.A.3(b) and it is this which must be integrated to obtain the total power transmitted from a unit white noise source.

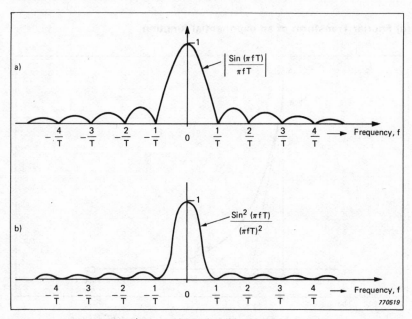

Fig.A3. (a) $|sin\ x/x|$ (b) sin^2x/x^2 where $x = \pi fT$

Thus, the total area under the power transmission curve:

$$= \int_{-\infty}^{\infty} \frac{sin^2(\pi fT)}{(\pi fT)^2} \, df$$

$$= \int_{-\infty}^{\infty} \frac{sin^2 x}{x^2} \cdot \frac{df}{dx} \cdot dx \quad , \qquad \text{where } x = \pi fT$$

$$= \frac{1}{\pi T} \int_{-\infty}^{\infty} \frac{sin^2 x}{x^2} \, dx \qquad\qquad\qquad (A.4)$$

From tables of standard integrals, the value of the integral is found to be π, resulting in a total area of $1/T$. Since the peak amplitude was normalised to unity, dividing by this gives:

$$B_{\text{eff}} = \frac{1}{T} \qquad \text{as stated in Eqn. } (2.23)$$

(d) Fourier Transform of an exponential function

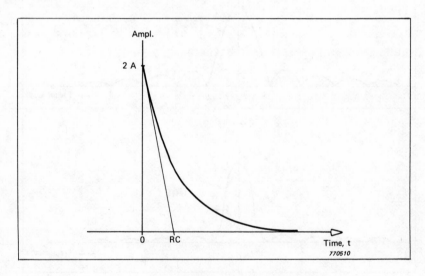

Fig.A4. Decaying exponential $2Ae^{-t/RC}$

Fig.A.4 depicts the exponential function defined by:

220

$$g(t) = 2Ae^{-t/RC} \quad , \quad t \geqslant 0$$
$$= 0 \quad , \quad otherwise$$

(A.5)

Thus, from Eqn.(2.14) its Fourier Transform is given by:

$$G(f) = 2A \int_0^\infty e^{-t/RC} e^{-j2\pi ft} \, dt$$

$$= 2A \int_0^\infty e^{-((1/RC) + j2\pi f)t} \, dt$$

$$= -\frac{2A}{\left(\dfrac{1}{RC} + j2\pi f\right)} \left[e^{-((1/RC) + j2\pi f)t} \right]_0^\infty$$

$$= \frac{2ARC}{1 + j2\pi fRC}$$

(A.6)

The peak amplitude of this function, occurring where $f = 0$, is thus given by $A(2RC)$ which will be seen to be the same as for the spectrum of the rectangular function (Eqn. A.3) if $T = 2RC$.

(e) Bandwidth of the spectrum of a decaying exponential

Normalising the function of Eqn. (A.6) to a peak value of unity gives $1/(1 + j\pi f2RC)$ which can be expressed as

$$\frac{1 - j\pi f\, 2RC}{1 + (\pi f\, 2RC)^2}$$

The modulus squared of this function is:

$$\frac{1}{1 + (\pi f\, 2RC)^2}$$

and the total integral under this power transmission curve is

$$\int_{-\infty}^{\infty} \frac{df}{1 + (\pi f\, 2RC)^2} = \frac{1}{\pi\, 2RC} \int_{-\infty}^{\infty} \frac{dx}{1 + x^2} \quad , \quad where\ x = \pi f\, 2RC$$

$$\left(\because \frac{df}{dx} = \frac{1}{\pi\, 2RC} \right)$$

From tables of standard integrals the value of the infinite integral is π and thus the total area under the curve is $1/2RC$.

The effective bandwidth is obtained by dividing this by the peak value (unity) and thus:

$$B_{eff} = \frac{1}{2RC} \tag{A.7}$$

as illustrated in Fig.3.13.

(f) The Convolution Theorem

Referring to Section 2.5.3, it is given that:

$$G(f) = \int_{-\infty}^{\infty} g(t)e^{-j2\pi ft}\, dt \tag{A.8}$$

$$F(f) = \int_{-\infty}^{\infty} f(t)e^{-j2\pi ft}\, dt \tag{A.9}$$

$$H(f) = \int_{-\infty}^{\infty} h(t)e^{-j2\pi ft}\, dt \tag{A.10}$$

and $\quad g(t) = f(t) * h(t) = \int_{-\infty}^{\infty} f(\tau)h(t-\tau)\, d\tau \tag{A.11}$

Substituting Eqn. (A.11) in (A.8) gives

$$G(f) = \int_{-\infty}^{\infty} \left[\int_{-\infty}^{\infty} f(\tau)h(t-\tau)\, d\tau \right] e^{-j2\pi ft}\, dt$$

which by reversing the order of integration gives:

$$G(f) = \int_{-\infty}^{\infty} f(\tau) \left[\int_{-\infty}^{\infty} h(t-\tau)e^{-j2\pi ft}\, dt \right] d\tau$$

$$= \int_{-\infty}^{\infty} f(\tau) \left[\int_{-\infty}^{\infty} h(u)e^{-j2\pi f(u+\tau)}\, du \right] d\tau$$

where $u = t-\tau$ (and thus $du = dt$)

This reduces to:

222

$$G(f) = \left[\int_{-\infty}^{\infty} f(\tau)e^{-j2\pi f\tau}\, d\tau\right]\left[\int_{-\infty}^{\infty} h(u)e^{-j2\pi fu}\, du\right]$$

which by substituting Equations (A.9) and (A.10) gives:

$$G(f) = F(f) \cdot H(f) \qquad \textit{as stated in Eqn. (2.31)}$$

APPENDIX B

Mean Square Error for Narrow Band Random Noise

The development given here basically follows that of Ref.3.1 but makes use of concepts developed in Chapter 2 to clarify the argument.

A narrow band stationary random signal of bandwidth B is considered, such as would be passed by an ideal filter of bandwidth B from a white noise source. Fig.B.1(a) illustrates the power spectrum of this signal which has a constant power spectral density W_B within the passband. (Note that the 2-sided spectrum representation is assumed.)

The complex spectrum corresponding to Fig.B.1(a) (i.e. the direct Fourier transform of the time signal $g(t)$) may be termed $G(f)$ and has the properties:

$$\left.\begin{array}{l} |G(f)|^2 = W_B \\ \angle G(f) = \text{random} \end{array}\right\} \text{inside the passbands}$$

$$\left.\begin{array}{l} |G(f)|^2 = 0 \\ \angle G(f) = \text{undefined} \end{array}\right\} \text{outside the passbands} \qquad (B.1)$$

When the signal $g(t)$ is passed through a squaring circuit to obtain its power, the resulting multiplication in the time domain ($g(t) \times g(t)$) transforms by the Fourier transform to a convolution in the frequency domain (see Section 2.5.3).

Thus, from Eqn.2.30 the frequency spectrum of $g^2(t)$ $(= y(t))$ will be given by:

$$Y(f) = \int_{-\infty}^{\infty} G(\phi) G(f-\phi) \, d\phi \qquad (B.2)$$

The evaluation of this convolution integral must be treated separately for the two cases:

(1) Displacement frequency $f = {}^{\flat}0$
(2) Displacement frequency $f \neq 0$

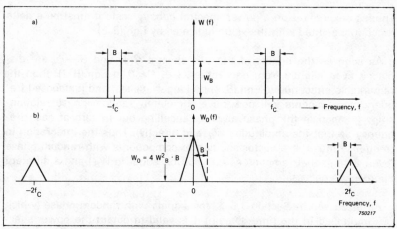

Fig.B1. *Sketches illustrating the effect of squaring a narrow frequency band of random noise.*
a) The noise frequency spectrum before squaring
b) The output spectrum from the squaring device

For $f = 0$, Equation (B.2) reduces to

$$Y_{DC}(0) = \int_{-\infty}^{\infty} G(\phi) G(-\phi) \, d\phi \tag{B.3}$$

Since $g(t)$ is real, its spectrum $G(\phi)$ is conjugate even (c. f. Eqn.(2.12) for periodic signals) and thus:

$$G(-\phi) = G^*(\phi) \tag{B.4}$$

Substituting in Eqn.(B.3) gives:

$$Y_{DC}(0) = \int_{-\infty}^{\infty} G(\phi) . G^*(\phi) \, d\phi$$

$$= \int_{-\infty}^{\infty} |G(\phi)|^2 \, d\phi$$

$$= 2 \int_{f_c - B/2}^{f_c + B/2} W_B \, d\phi, \text{ making use of Eqns. (B.1)}$$

$$= 2BW_B \tag{B.5}$$

Y_{DC} (0) is of course the DC component of the squared signal, and considering its dimensions (PSD × bandwidth) it obviously has finite power.

225

Thus, to express it on a power spectral *density* scale it must be a delta function weighted with the value indicated by Eqn.(B.5).

As soon as the origins of the two spectra $G(\phi)$ and $G(-\phi)$ are displaced even slightly from each other, i.e. $f \neq 0$ in Eqn.(B.2), then the remarkable effect due to Eqn.(B.4) no longer applies, and juxtaposed frequency components will now have completely random phase relationships (instead of the phase always cancelling out to zero at each frequency so that the amplitudes W_B add directly). Thus the integration in frequency must be a vector addition of components with random phase (even though their amplitudes will still be equal to W_B) and a different approach is necessary.

As discussed in Section 3.5.3, for signals with random phase (which are multiplied in the time domain) it is valid to obtain the power spectral density of the result by convolving the individual PSD spectra. Fig.B.1(b) indicates the results of doing this for the spectrum of Fig.B.1(a). The central triangular portion results from the fact that the greater the displacement of the two identical power spectra, the less the overlap of the rectangular passbands, the result decreasing linearly down to zero at a displacement equal to the bandwidth B (zero overlap). The two smaller triangles occur similarly when the positive frequency passband of one spectrum coincides with the negative frequency passband of the other. In fact it is not strictly true that the power spectra are convolved in this case because of the symmetry which exists about zero frequency, even when the two complex spectra $G(\phi)$ and $G(-\phi)$ are displaced. (This would not be the case if $g(t)$ were multiplied by a different signal with the same PSD.) The scaling of the result can be determined by considering the limiting case as displacement frequency $f \rightarrow 0$.

For the maximum value of the distributed portion of the spectrum (as opposed to the DC component already obtained), Eqn.(B.2) gives:

$$Y_{AC}(0) = \lim_{f \to 0} \int_{-\infty}^{\infty} G(\phi) G(f - \phi) \, d\phi \qquad (B.6)$$

The difference with respect to Eqn.(B.3) is that although the amplitude of the vector to be integrated is still $|G(f)|^2$ $(= W_B)$ its phase angle is random (however small f is). Thus, considering the positive frequencies only, the amplitude of the vector resulting from the integral of Eqn.(B.6) will add according to the *square root* of the range of the integration and thus equals $W_B \sqrt{B}$. Because of symmetry, it is found that the resultant vector from the negative frequency side has *exactly the same phase angle* (Fig.B2) and so the amplitude of the total integral is

226

equal to $2W_B \sqrt{B}$. The peak value of the power spectrum of the result (as shown in Fig.B.1(b)) is thus the square of this or

$$|Y_{AC}(0)|^2 = 4W_B^2 B \qquad (B.7)$$

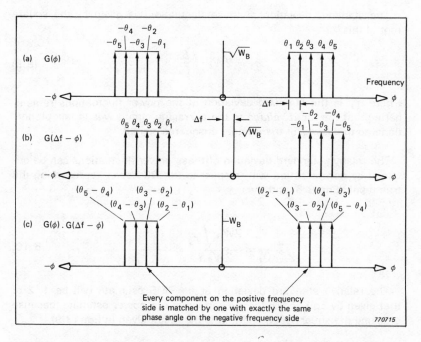

Fig.B2. (a) Spectrum $G(\phi)$ of narrow band random noise, showing amplitude $\sqrt{W_B}$ and indicating (random) phase angles θ_i
(b) Reversed and displaced spectrum $G(\Delta f - \phi)$
(c) Product $G(\phi) \cdot G(\Delta f - \phi)$ which is to be integrated to obtain convolution for $f = \Delta f$

The continuous spectrum of Fig.B.1(b) can be said to represent the AC fluctuations of the squared signal around the DC component which represents the long-term average. The fluctuations can be reduced by low-pass filtering, and Fig.B.3 shows the effect of doing this with an averaging network whose lowpass filter bandwidth is $\ll B$. Over a small frequency range in the vicinity of zero frequency the spectrum level can be considered constant, and equal to the value at zero frequency $(4 W_B^2 B)$. Thus, the AC power transmitted by an averaging network of bandwidth $1/T_A$ (and thus with effective averaging time T_A,

227

see Appendix A) is obtained by integrating the PSD of the fluctuations over the bandwidth, and is given by

$$\text{AC power} = 4W_B^2 \frac{B}{T_A} \qquad (B.8)$$

The standard deviation of these fluctuations is given by the square root of this, or

$$\sigma_1 = 2W_B \sqrt{\frac{B}{T_A}} \qquad (B.9)$$

where σ_1 is the standard deviation of the power fluctuations (remembering that the input *voltage* to the averaging circuit was in fact proportional to the *power* of the original unsquared signal).

The relative standard deviation of these power fluctuations can be obtained by normalisation with respect to the DC power representing the true result (Eqn.B.5) and thus:

$$\frac{\sigma_1}{Y_{DC}(0)} = \frac{2W_B \sqrt{\frac{B}{T_A}}}{2W_B B} = \frac{1}{\sqrt{BT_A}} \qquad (B.10)$$

The relative standard deviation of an RMS estimate will be $1/2$ of that given by Eqn.(B.10) for a mean square or power estimate (because of taking the square root) and that is the result given in Eqn.(3.9).

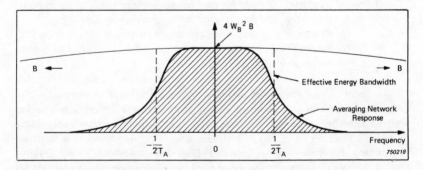

Fig.B3. The low-frequency portion of the squared signal spectrum shown with expanded frequency scale, together with the effect of passing the spectrum through an averaging network

REFERENCES

Chapter 1 — Introduction

1.1. A. Papoulis, *The Fourier Integral and its Applications*. Mc Graw-Hill, 1962.

Chapter 2 — Theoretical Analysis

2.1. G. M. Jenkins & D. G. Watts, *Spectral Analysis and its Applications*. Holden-Day, San Francisco, 1968.

2.2. J. S. Bendat & A. G. Piersol, *Random Data: Analysis and Measurement Procedures*. Wiley — Interscience, 1971.

2.3. E. O. Brigham, *The Fast Fourier Transform*, Prentice-Hall, N. J., 1974.

Chapter 3 — Analog Analysis

3.1. C. G. Wahrman & J. T. Broch, "On the Averaging Time of RMS Measurements", *B & K Technical Review*, Nos. 2 & 3, 1975.

3.2. C. G. Wahrman, "RMS and LMS Circuit Developments" *B & K Technical Review*, to be published.

3.3. J. T. Broch & C. G. Wahrman, "Effective Averaging Time of the Level Recorder Type 2305". *B & K Technical Review* No. 1, 1961.

3.4. R. B. Randall, "High Speed Narrow Band Analysis using the Digital Event Recorder Type 7502". *B & K Technical Review* No. 2, 1973.

3.5. R. B. Randall, "High Speed Narrow Band Analysis with Digital Output". B & K Application Note, No. 12—192.

3.6. E. A. Sloane, "Comparison of Linearly and Quadratically Modified Spectral Estimates of Gaussian Signals". *IEEE Trans. Audio & Electroacoustics*, Vol. AU—17 No. 2, June 1969. pp. 133—137.

3.7. J. T. Broch & H. P. Olesen, "On the Frequency Analysis of Mechanical Shocks and Single Impulses". *B & K Technical Review*, No. 3, 1970.

3.8. J. T. Broch, "Analog Analysis of Shocks", 7th ICA, Budapest, 1971. Paper No. 20 V6.

3.9. C. G. Wahrman, "Averaging Time of Measurements". B & K Application Note No. 11—138.

Chapter 4 — Digital Filters

4.1. A. V. Oppenheim & R. W. Schafer, *Digital Signal Processing* Prentice-Hall, N. J., 1975.

4.2. L. R. Rabiner & B. Gold, *Theory and Application of Digital Signal Processing.* Prentice-Hall, N. J., 1975.

4.3. The Institute of Electrical and Electronics Engineers, Inc. *IEEE Standard Digital Interface for Programmable Instrumentation,* 1975.

4.4. R. Upton, "Automated Measurements of Reverberation Time using the Digital Frequency Analyzer Type 2131." *B & K Technical Review,* No. 2, 1977.

Chapter 5 — FFT

5.1. J. W. Cooley & J. W. Tukey, "An Algorithm for the Machine Calculation of Complex Fourier Series", *Math. of Comp.*, Vol. 19, No. 90, pp 297—301, 1965.

5.2. "Special Issue on the Fast Fourier Transform", *IEEE Trans. Audio & Electroacoustics,* Vol. AU—15, June 1967.

5.3. J. W. Cooley, P. A. W. Lewis & P. D. Welch, "The Fast Fourier

Transform Algorithm: Programming Considerations in the Calculation of Sine, Cosine and Laplace Transforms". *J. Sound Vib.* (1970) Vol. 12 No. 3 pp. 315—337.

Chapter 6 — Advanced Analysis

6.1. H. K. Kohler, A. Pratt & A. M. Thompson, "Dynamics and Noise of Parallel-axis Gearing" in *Gearing in 1970*, I. Mech. E., London, 1970.

6.2. D. R. Houser & M. J. Drosjack, "Vibration Signal Analysis Techniques". NTIS Publ. No. AD-776 397. 5825 Port Royal Rd, Springfield, Va., USA, Dec. 1973.

6.3. C. A. Mercer, "Note on Digital Estimation of Correlation Functions". *J. Sound Vib.*, Vol. 27, No. 2, 1973 pp. 262—265.

6.4. P. Eilers & A. J. Francken, Comment on Ref. 6.3 (also reply by author), *J. Sound Vib.*, Vol. 31, No. 3, 1973 pp. 383—389.

6.5. T. G. Stockham, Jr. "High-speed Convolution and Correlation with Applications to Digital Filtering". Chapter 7 in *Digital Processing of Signals* by B. Gold & C. M. Rader, McGraw-Hill, 1969.

6.6. B. P. Bogert, M.J.R. Healy & J. W. Tukey, "The Quefrency Alanysis of Time Series for Echoes: Cepstrum, Pseudo-Autocovariance, Cross-cepstrum and Saphe Cracking", in *Proceedings of the Symposium on Time Series Analysis*, by M. Rosenblatt, (Ed.), Wiley N. Y. 1963, pp. 209—243.

6.7. J. Trampe Broch, "On the Applicability and Limitations of the Cross-Correlation and the Cross-Spectral Density Techniques", *B & K Technical Review* No. 4, 1970.

6.8. A. M. Noll, "Cepstrum Pitch Determination", *J.A.S.A.* Vol. 41, No. 2, 1967, pp. 293—309.

6.9. J. K. Hammond & L. G. Peardon, "The Power Cepstrum applied to Multi-peaked wavelets". *J. Sound Vib.*, Vol. 48, No. 4, 1976 pp. 537—541.

6.10. G. Sapy, "Diagnostic Vibratoire des Ruptures d'Aubes Mobiles de Turbines à Vapeur", Paper presented at the Conference on Monitoring Diagnostics in Industry, Prague, August 1975. Dům Techniky, Gorkého nám. 23, Prague 1.

6.11. R. B. Randall, "Gearbox Fault Diagnosis using Cepstrum Analysis". *Proc. IVth World Congr. Theory of Machines and Mechanisms.* Vol. 1, pp. 169—174. I. Mech. E., London, 1975.

6.12. A. V. Oppenheim, R. W. Schafer & T. G. Stockham, "Nonlinear Filtering of Multiplied and Convolved Signals", *IEEE Trans. Audio & Electroacoustics,* Vol. AU-16, No. 3, Sept. 1968.

6.13. T. J. Ulrych, "Application of Homomorphic Deconvolution to Seismology", *Geophys.,* Vol. 36, No. 4, Aug. 1971, pp. 650—660.

6.14. T. E. Siddon, "Surface Di-pole Strength by Cross-correlation Method", *JASA,* Vol. 53, No. 2, 1973 pp. 619—633.

6.15. L. D. Enochson & R. K. Otnes, *Programming and Analysis for Digital Time Series Data.* Shock & Vibration Monograph SVM-3, Shock and Vibration Center, Naval Research Lab., Washington.

6.16. SEECO '77, "Signal Processing for Vibration, Shock & Noise". Transactions of Conference at Imperial College, London, April 1977. Society of Environmental Engineers, England.

6.17. W. G. Halvorsen & J. S. Bendat, "Noise Source Identification using Coherent Output Power Spectra". *Sound & Vibration* August, 1975, pp. 15—24.

6.18. J. S. Bendat, "Solutions for the Multiple Input/Output Problem". *J. Sound Vib.,* Vol. 44, No. 3, 1976, pp. 311—325.

6.19. J. S. Bendat, "System Identification from Multiple Input/Output Data". *J. Sound Vib.,* Vol. 49, No. 3, 1976 pp. 293—308.

6.20. A. F. Seybert & M. J. Crocker, "The Use of Coherence Techniques to Predict the Effect of Engine Operating Parameters on Diesel Engine Noise". *J. Eng. for Ind., Trans. ASME,* Nov. 1975, pp. 1227—1233.

INDEX

233

234